THE BRITISH COUNCIL COLLECTION 1984–1994

The British Council Collection

1984–1994

DUBLIN

Donated to

**Visual Art Degree
Sherkin Island**

The British Council

cover
ALAN GOUK
Eyelash Swoop 1985–87
P5579

Text © The British Council 1995
Illustrations © The artists or their estates
The British Council acknowledges with
thanks the permission given by artists or
their estates to reproduce the works
illustrated in this catalogue.

ISBN 0 86355 290 0

Published by The British Council,
10 Spring Gardens,
London SW1A 2BN

Designed by Robert Dalrymple and
Caroline Johnston

Printed by BAS Printers Limited,
Over Wallop, Stockbridge, Hampshire

Photographic credits

Graziano Arici, Venice
Birmingham Museum and Art Gallery
Gordon Bishop
David Cripps
Prudence Cuming Associates Ltd.
Charles Meecham
George Meyrick
Newbery Smith Photography
Ram Rahman, New Delhi
Antonia Reeve
John Riddy
Morten Thorkildsen, Oslo
Rodney Todd-White & Son
Christopher Warde-Jones, Rome
Gareth Winters
Edward Woodman
Jerry Young

Contents

Acknowledgements

Catalogue researched and edited by Diana Eccles and Barbara Putt.

The Editors would like to thank Julius Breeze, Kaylee Coxall, Joanna Gutteridge, Craig Henderson, Lesley Johnson, Victorine F-Martineau, Judith Monk, Richard Riley, and Muriel Wilson for their valuable assistance.

Particular thanks are due to Kathy Niblett of Stoke-on-Trent City Museum and Art Gallery for her specialist advice. Thanks are also due to Wendy Evans of the Museum of London, Ian Jeffrey, Lynn Miller of the Wedgwood Museum, Barlaston, and Helen Spencer of Birmingham Museum and Art Gallery.

Foreword

To celebrate the British Council's 50th Anniversary in 1984, Henry Moore presented over 200 graphics to the British Council Collection. This magnificent gift came too late to record in the first volume of the catalogue (published in 1984) but I am delighted that they are fully documented here. The Collection has benefited greatly from the generosity of artists over the years and I should like particularly to thank Gillian Ayres, Sir Anthony Caro and Lynn Chadwick for donating important works in recent years.

Most purchasing for the Collection is made from a small annual grant, the limited nature of which dictates that work is generally bought from artists in early or mid-career, rarely from artists with established international reputations. On occasion, however, the purchase grant is supplemented by savings found from elsewhere in the British Council, enabling us to buy major works by artists such as Patrick Caulfield, Richard Hamilton, R B Kitaj and Bill Woodrow. Other funds have sometimes been available to buy works for specific buildings, for example the British Council's new headquarters in New Delhi for which works by Peter Kinley, Dhruva Mistry and Boyd Webb, have been acquired. In all this we are guided by the British Council Collection and Purchasing Sub-Committee, made up of the Chairman and three members of the Visual Arts Advisory Committee. I should like to thank them for their invaluable advice, which has led to the formation of a Collection of which we are proud, and which does such an effective job of presenting the strength and vitality of British art abroad.

Sir John Hanson
Director-General
The British Council

Introduction

This catalogue documents nearly one thousand works acquired for the British Council Collection between 1984–1994. The most recent to be recorded is Douglas Gordon's *"10 ms^{-1}"*, the first video installation to enter the Collection and a sign of the Collection's increasing ability to encompass the new technologies with which many younger artists are working. Gordon initially produced this work on videotape, a medium prone to malfunction. Advances in technology have enabled us to transfer this to laser disc, more robust and therefore better suited to life as part of the British Council Collection.

For the Collection travels globally and extensively. It is the only collection in Britain designed to promote the achievements of British art abroad, which it does through constant re-formulation into exhibitions and displays. In its early days (started in 1935, a year after the founding of the British Council), much of it was bought with the aim of making small exhibitions of works on paper, for long-term touring, often in less accessible countries. Their modest scale and flat packing guaranteed that they would fit inside the hold of an aircraft or guard's van worldwide, and that they could be assembled and installed by almost anyone. These considerations have largely gone. During her period as Curator (1985–1989), Teresa Gleadowe reviewed the nature and role of Circulating Exhibitions, the term given to the 25 or so exhibitions made up from the Collection in any one year. Her findings showed that while there was still interest in these shows, the demand was for more wide-ranging exhibitions, dealing in up-to-date developments, accompanied by substantial publications. Accordingly, greater emphasis has been given to acquiring unique works as opposed to multiples, to make up Circulating Exhibitions such as *Cries & Whispers* and *New Voices*, both focusing on paintings by young artists (under the age of 35 at the date of purchase). A third in this series is now in preparation.

Other factors, such as the re-drawing of the map of Central and Eastern Europe and the economic boom in the Far East, have affected the uses of the Collection over the past decade and, to some extent, its composition. Eastern Bloc countries were rarely able to host exhibitions of contemporary art from abroad, although the Council maintained contact with artists and curators through a restricted programme of exchanges. Today, Circulating Exhibitions are in demand throughout Central and Eastern Europe, forcing the pace, increasing the pressure to tour longer, further and to regions with little previous knowledge of British art. Last year was the first in which works from the Collection toured to Russian cities and towns along the Volga, such as Ivanov and Yaroslavl. Later this year (1995) our first Circulating Exhibition will reach Albania.

In the Far East, the building of a vast network of galleries and museums, fed by the communications revolution and nourished by a voracious marketplace, has led to an appetite for art of all sorts, especially contemporary. Many works purchased for the Collection over the past decade might once have been considered 'impractical': Andy Goldsworthy's *Sweet chestnut leaf horn* (leaves), Cornelia Parker's *Falling* (silver plated trophies and dish-wire), Chris Ofili's *Painting with Shit on it* (elephant dung) and Rachel Whiteread's *False Door* (plaster). But the sophistication of the new museum network, its insistence on seeing new work now (not waiting for the packet boat to bring it years later) and the huge variety of materials in which artists now work have encouraged the purchase of some more fragile or vulnerable works;

though these tend to end up on long loan to museums or galleries abroad, rather than in touring exhibitions.

Another factor influencing the shape of the Collection over the past decade has been the introduction of photography. Before 1982, photography was handled elsewhere in the British Council, and then only as reportage or documentary. It has been this Department's task to present British photography abroad as an essential element of British art, as a distinctive but not separate part. This has been achieved chiefly through the energy and foresight of Brett Rogers, who joined Visual Arts Department as an Exhibition Officer in 1982, with a remit to develop its photography policy. Fifteen exhibitions drawn from photography purchased for the Collection during this period have been on worldwide tour.

The crafts have been less systematically pursued, possibly because until the Department was re-named Visual Arts Department (having been Fine Arts for the previous 50 or so years), their acquisition had not been thought a priority. They first became a feature of the Department's work during the war, when they were used to illustrate to 'the Dominions and certain foreign countries' the extraordinary levels of skill that were in danger of extinction should those countries not come to Britain's aid. The work of putting together such exhibitions fell to Muriel Rose, who had unrivalled expertise in the field. She acquired for the Collection examples of china services decorated by Edward Bawden, Eric Ravilious and Graham Sutherland, weavings by Ethel Mairet, Enid Marx and Marianne Straub, studio pottery by Michael Cardew, Hans Coper, Bernard Leach and Lucie Rie, and fine printing by the Golden Cockerel Press. Sadly, much of this material was de-accessioned following a policy review in the 1960s. What remains is documented here, since it was excluded from the first volume of the Collection catalogue, published in 1984. Together with the craft items mostly purchased by Muriel Wilson during the 1980s and early 1990s, this now presents a complete record of the existing craft holdings.

Since 1986, the Collection has been designated a 'national collection', bringing with it the responsibility to hold and maintain works for the nation, preventing it from being broken up for financial or other gain. Given the fate of so many of the craft items, this is a salutary affirmation of the Collection's value to the nation, as well as a hedge against short-termism. For shifts in perspective are integral to the nature of collections and one of the chief reasons why de-accessioning should be looked on with caution. Today's curator is also the custodian of tomorrow's inheritance and it does not seem to me to be a curator's job to interpret history by the light of fashionable management criteria which, in any case, are going to be far more unfashionable in a number of years than any works of art that might currently be deemed disposable. The difference, as Coco Chanel put it, between art and fashion is that the former increases in value and significance while the latter diminishes.

At the time of writing, over 2500 works from the 6500 that constitute the Collection are in exhibitions overseas, with a further 2500 on display throughout the British Council estate, located on 300 sites in the 109 countries in which the Council is represented. Over the past decade there has been increasing awareness of the role the Collection plays in presenting British art worldwide and the way it makes visible the achievements of British artists to an international audience. This may partly have come about through the British Council's espousal of a 'percent for art' policy, whereby a percentage of all building or refurbishment costs is set aside specifically for works of art. Certainly the major commissions to Howard Hodgkin and Stephen Cox for the British Council's new headquarters in New Delhi, and to Patrick Caulfield and Bill Woodrow for its new Northern headquarters in Manchester are outstanding. They are landmarks which, like the rest of the works in the Collection, from the most prominent sculpture to the slightest sketch, are not only of national value, but an immense international asset.

This catalogue has been researched, compiled and edited by Diana Eccles, the Collections Manager, and Barbara Putt, until recently the Department's Research Officer. They have been painstaking in ensuring that entries under each item are accurate and complete to the greatest possible degree, a task often complicated – though not defied – by the many thousands of miles separating them from the objects in question. I should like to take this opportunity of thanking them both most warmly for their indefatigable efforts on behalf of all the artists and their work represented in this catalogue.

Andrea Rose
Head of Visual Arts

Cataloguers' Note

Care has been taken to ensure that the entries are accurate. However, in the case of a few works on tour at the time of writing, it has not been possible to verify artists' inscriptions or the surface dimensions of framed works.

All enquiries relating to to the works documented in this catalogue, and those included in *The British Council Collection 1938–1984*, published by The British Council in 1984 (ISBN 0 86355 020 7 hardback, 0 86355 021 5 softback), should be addressed to:

The Collections Manager
Visual Arts Department
The British Council
11 Portland Place
London W1N 4EJ

PART I : **Original Works**

Entries are arranged by artist in alphabetical order. Where an artist has more than one work in the Collection, the works are given in chronological order. Works of the same year are listed in British Council Collection accession number sequence, unless the actual day or month of completion is known.

1. Name of artist and date of birth (and death).

2. Title of work.

3. Date of work.

4. Medium.

5. Dimensions are given in centimetres, height preceding width and depth. Unless otherwise stated, the dimensions are of the original surface, without mount or frame.

6. Signatures and full inscriptions are noted, with abbreviations to indicate their position e.g. TRC – top right corner, BE – bottom edge.

7. Source and date of acquisition.

8. British Council Collection accession number.

ABRAHAMS Ivor B 1935
Seated Girl 1984

Collage on blue paper, 74.5 × 54.5
Inscribed BLC: *Ivor Abrahams 84*; verso
BLC: *Seated Girl*
Purchased from Bernard Jacobson
Gallery January 1985
P4997

ABRAHAMS Ivor B 1935
Reclining Figure I 1984

Bronze – Edition 1/4, 29 × 20 × 6.8
Purchased from Bernard Jacobson
Gallery January 1985
P4998

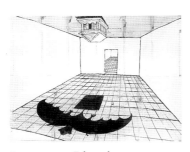

ALLINGTON Edward B 1951
The Daughters of the Night 1982

Ink and emulsion on paper, 54 × 74.5
Inscribed verso TL: *the daughters of the
night 1982 Edward Allington*
Presented anonymously October 1992
P6097 (colour plate 1)

ANDREWS Michael 1928–1995
**Recollection of a Moment in
October 1989 – The Tobasnich
Burn, Glenartney** 1992

Oil on gesso on board, 30.5 × 25.4
Inscribed verso: "*Recollection of a
moment in Oct. 1989 .. The* TOBASNICH
*Burn; Glenart oil on board 12″ × 10″
(gesso ground) Michael Andrews '92*
Purchased from Anthony d'Offay
Gallery December 1992
P6132 (colour plate 2)

ATKINS Ray B 1937
Green Gorse 1991

Oil on board, 134.6 × 122
Inscribed on T batten: *Summer 91 A.*;
verso T centre: *Gorse bush in summer*;
verso centre: *Summer 91 Ray Atkins*
Purchased from Art Space Gallery –
Michael Richardson Contemporary Art
October 1993
P6197

ATKINSON Terry B 1939
**Art for the Bunker 7: Bunker in
Armagh 11: Ancient Gaelic Ghost
after completing a Tour of Duty
passing through an Ideological
Decontamination Shower before
going off duty. Note the Easter
Cactus (left) and Easter Lilies and
how brightly the Candles
continue to burn** 1985

Pastel and conté on paper, 120 × 107.5
Purchased at The Whitechapel Auction,
Sotheby's July 1987
P5508 (colour plate 3)

AUERBACH Frank B 1931
Head of JYM III 1980

Oil on board, 71.1 × 61
Purchased from Marlborough Fine Art
January 1985
P4995

AUERBACH Frank B 1931
Tree on Primrose Hill 1984–85

Oil on canvas, 122.6 × 148.6
Inscribed on stretcher TL: *Auerbach
PRIMROSE HILL 1984 1985*; on stretcher
TR: *PRIMROSE HILL 1984–85*
Purchased from Marlborough Fine Art
March 1986
P5359 (colour plate 4)

AUSTEN David B 1960
An old man in a dry month 1985

Ink and collage on paper, 51 × 40.5
Inscribed BLC: "*An old man in a dry
month" David Austen 17.6.85*
Purchased from Anthony Reynolds
Gallery October 1985
P5303

AUSTEN David B 1960
Profile of a priest 1985

Ink and collage on paper, 51 × 40.5
Inscribed BLC: '*profile of a priest*'
D. Austen 19.6.85
Purchased from Anthony Reynolds
Gallery October 1985

P5302

AUSTEN David B 1960
Sleeping on the wind 1989

Oil on linen, 40.6 × 35.5
Purchased from Anderson O'Day
Gallery October 1990

P5830

AUSTEN David B 1960
Be with her lost 1991

Oil on linen, 91.4 × 81.2
Inscribed TL on top turnover of canvas:
D. Austen 91
Purchased from Anthony Reynolds
Gallery July 1992

P6079

AYRES Gillian B 1930
Makar Sankranti 1990

Collage on paper, incorporating paper
kites from Jaipur, 152.5 × 298
Inscribed BL: *Gillian Ayres 1990*
Presented by the artist May 1991

P5936

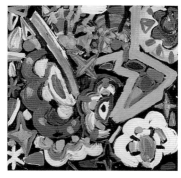

AYRES Gillian B 1930
Indian Summer 1990

Oil on canvas, 152 × 152
Inscribed BL: *Gillian Ayres*
Purchased from the artist April 1991

P6012

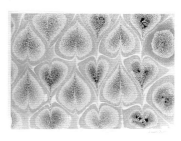

BAWDEN Edward 1903–1989
Leaf Patterns *c.*1954/1955

Inked leaf impressions: unique work
35.2 × 50
Inscribed BRC: *Edward Bawden*
Purchased from The Fine Art Society
October 1989

P5647

BENSON Tom B 1963
Untitled (green/ochre) 1989

Gouache on paper, 25 × 22.3
Inscribed BLC: *Jan 89*; BRC: *T Benson*
Purchased from the artist November
1989

P5738

BENSON Tom B 1963
Untitled (purple/orange) 1989

Gouache on paper, 24.7 × 22.3
Inscribed BLC: *Feb 89*; BRC: *T Benson*
Purchased from the artist November
1989

P5740

BENSON Tom B 1963
Untitled (blue/grey) 1989

Gouache on paper, 24.3 × 21.7
Inscribed BLC: *Jan 89*; BRC: *T Benson*
Purchased from the artist November
1989

P5739

BENSON Tom B 1963
Untitled (orange) 1989

Gouache on paper, 24.8 × 22.2
Inscribed BLC: *Feb 89*; BRC: *T Benson*
Purchased from the artist November
1989

P5741

BEVAN Tony B 1951
Tender Possessions 1986

Charcoal and pigment on canvas
210.5 × 119.5
Inscribed verso: *TENDER POSSESSIONS
1986 Tony Bevan*; and on stretcher: *Tony
Bevan 1986 Tender Possessions*
Purchased from Matt's Gallery, London
October 1986
P5424

BLACKETT Vivien B 1955
Tower, scarf 1987

Oil on canvas, 99 × 114
Inscribed verso BRC: *Vivien Blackett 1987*
Purchased from the artist August 1987
P5513

BLAKE Peter B 1932
Robin* 1994

Watercolour on paper, 15.1 × 12.6
Inscribed BRC: *Peter Blake. 1994.*; verso
T: *ROBIN*
Purchased from the artist October 1994
P6286
*This work was commissioned for the
British Council's 1994 Christmas card

BOYCE Sonia B 1962
Pillowcase 1990

Fabric dye, pen and crayon on cotton
155.9 × 195
Purchased from Vanessa Devereux
Gallery January 1992
P6008 (colour plate 5)

BOYD & EVANS
BOYD Fionnuala B 1944
EVANS Leslie B 1945
Looking back 1988

Crayon on paper, 56 × 85
Inscribed BLC: '*Looking back*'; BRC: *Boyd
& Evans 88*
Purchased from Angela Flowers Gallery
May 1988
P5589

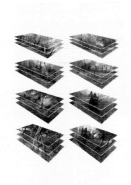

BRICK Michael B 1946
Northumberland Landscape 1983

Watercolour on paper, 89 × 71
Inscribed BRC: *Michael Brick '83*
Purchased from Anne Berthoud Gallery
August 1984
P4902

BRICK Michael B 1946
Autumn Landscape 1 1984

Watercolour on paper, 33 × 27.5
Inscribed BRC: *Michael Brick '84*
Purchased from Anne Berthoud Gallery
August 1984
P4899

BRICK Michael B 1946
Autumn Landscape 2 1984

Watercolour on paper, 33 × 27.5
Inscribed BRC: *Michael Brick '84*
Purchased from Anne Berthoud Gallery
August 1984
P4900

BRICK Michael B 1946
Autumn Landscape 3 1984

Watercolour on paper, 33 × 27.5
Inscribed BRC: *Michael Brick '84*
Purchased from Anne Berthoud Gallery
August 1984
P4901

BRICK Michael B 1946
East Wood 3 1984

Acrylic on paper, 116 × 82.5
Inscribed BRC: *Michael Brick '84*
Purchased from Anne Berthoud Gallery
August 1984
P4903

CAMP Jeffery B 1923
Beaching the Boat 1976

Oil on canvas over board, 51.5 × 51.5
Inscribed centre R: *CAMP*
Purchased from the artist November
1992
P6060

CAMPBELL Steven B 1953
Painting on a Darwinian Theme
1986

Oil on canvas, 226 × 203
Purchased from Marlborough Fine Art
March 1987
P5483 (colour plate 6)

CAULFIELD Patrick B 1936
The Blue Posts 1989

Acrylic on canvas, 289.5 × 205.7
Inscribed verso: *THE BLUE POSTS*
PATRICK CAULFIELD
Purchased from Waddington Galleries
March 1990
P5802

CAMP Jeffery B 1923
Magpies, Beachy Head 1983

Watercolour on paper, 17.7 × 25
Inscribed BLC: *CAMP*
Purchased from the Contemporary Art
Society Market November 1986
P5431

CARO Anthony B 1924
Summer Table 1990

From **The Cascades** series
Steel, rusted and waxed, 121 × 211 × 107
Presented by the artist September 1994
P6314

CHADWICK Lynn B 1914
Back to Venice 1988

Bronze – Edition HC/9, 193 × 276 × 152
Presented by the artist August 1988
P6285

CAMP Jeffery B 1923
Hang gliding, Beachy Head 1983

Oil on board, 51 × 50.7
Purchased from the artist November
1992
P6059

CAULFIELD Patrick B 1936
Selected Grapes 1981

Acrylic and oil on canvas, 45.8 × 60.6
Inscribed verso B: *SELECTED GRAPES* Ⓐ
PATRICK CAULFIELD 1981
Purchased from Waddington Galleries
March 1985
P5025 (colour plate 7)

CHEVSKA Maria B 1948
Chrysalis (i) 1987

Oil, encaustic on linen, 71 × 71
Inscribed verso: *Maria Chevska 1987*
Purchased from Anderson O'Day
Gallery November 1989
P5694

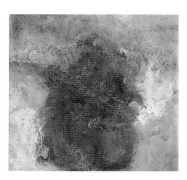

CHEVSKA Maria B 1948
Chrysalis (ii) 1988

Oil, encaustic on wood, 40 × 40.3
Purchased from Anderson O'Day
Gallery November 1989
P5693

COOPER Eileen B 1953
The Self and the Family 1984

Oil on canvas, 137 × 122
Inscribed verso TRC: *THE SELF AND THE*
FAMILY Eileen Cooper 1984
Purchased from Blond Fine Art
September 1984
P4905 (colour plate 8)

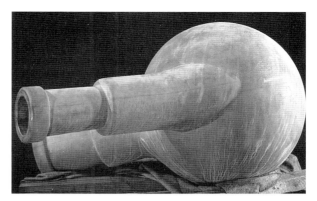

CRAGG Tony B 1949
Mother's Milk II 1988

Bronze cast, 90 × 192 × 142
Purchased from the artist December
1988
P5619

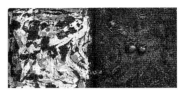

CRUMPLIN Colin B 1946
Cherries 1987

Acrylic and oil on canvas, 25.7 × 51.5
Inscribed verso: *Crumplin Cherries 1987*
Purchased from the artist May 1988
P5590

COHEN Andy B 1961
Bird Mobile 1985–86

Brazed steel, wire, tin and wood
33.9 × 23 × 16.1 (with base)
Inscribed on top of base: *ANDY 86*; on
underside of base: *Bird Mobile Andy 85*
Purchased from the artist October 1986
P5427

COVENTRY Keith B 1958
Nunhead Estate 1992

Oil on canvas, painted wood and glass
147 × 85.6
Purchased from Karsten Schubert,
London July 1992
P6080

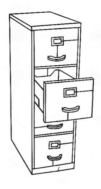

CRAIG-MARTIN, Michael B 1941
Filing Cabinet 1982

Welded steel, 74.9 × 37.4
Purchased from Nicola Jacobs Gallery
July 1987
P5512

CRUMPLIN Colin B 1946
Copper Tube 1988

Acrylic, oil and metal leaf on canvas
25.7 × 51.5
Inscribed verso: *Colin Crumplin Copper*
tube 4.88
Purchased from the artist May 1988
P5591

CONROY Stephen B 1964
Man of Vision 1987

Oil on canvas, 134.5 × 120
Inscribed BRC: ⓒ
Purchased from Conservation
Management October 1987
P5565

COX Stephen B 1946
Etruscan 1985

Granite
Four parts: each 55.9 × 35 × 10.2
Installation size: 55.9 × 304.8 × 10.2
Purchased from the artist March 1986
P5365

CURRIE Ken B 1960
Woman from Drumchapel 1986

Pastel on paper, 111 × 86
Inscribed BR: *"Woman from*
Drumchapel" 1986.; BRC: *K Currie*
Purchased from the artist September
1986
P5419

CURRIE Ken B 1960
The Self-Taught Man 1986

Ink, pencil and pastel on paper
116 × 103
Inscribed BRC: *"The Self-Taught Man"*
1986
Purchased from the artist July 1987
P5507

DE CAIRES Dennis B 1957
Singing Sandra 1989

Acrylic and oil on canvas, 25.5 × 25.5
Inscribed verso: *Singing Sandra Dennis
de Caires 1989*
Purchased from the artist June 1989
P5633

DENNIS Jeffrey B 1958
Heartwood 1989

Oil on canvas
Six panels: each 76 × 107
Overall size: 230 × 214
Inscribed lower left panel BLC: *Dennis
1989 Heartwood*; each panel inscribed
verso: *Dennis 1989 'Heartwood'*, plus an
installation diagram and instructions
Purchased from Salvatore Ala Gallery,
New York March 1991
P5893

DONNELLY Micky B 1952
Connolly's Hat with Lilies 1987

Oil on canvas, 152.4 × 152.4
Inscribed verso TLC: *CONNOLLY'S HAT
WITH LILIES*
Purchased from Fenderesky Gallery,
Belfast July 1987
P5505

DAVENPORT Ian B 1966
Untitled Grey II 1990

Undercoat and varnish on canvas
213.4 × 213.4
Purchased from Waddington Galleries
October 1990
P5831

DE MONCHAUX Cathy B 1960
Hold 1988

Lead, velvet and bolts, 25 × 114.5 × 12.5
Purchased from the artist February 1991
P5861

DOIG Peter B 1959
Hill Houses 1990–91

Oil on canvas, 199.9 × 239
Inscribed verso upper L: *PETER DOIG
Dec. 1990/91 'HILL HOUSE'S'*
Purchased from Serpentine Gallery
February 1991
P5866

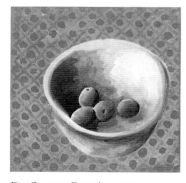

DE CAIRES Dennis B 1957
Evening Fruit 1988–89

Acrylic and oil on canvas, 25.5 × 25.5
Inscribed verso: *Evening Fruit Dennis de
Caires 1988–89*
Purchased from the artist June 1989
P5634

DENIS Dominic B 1963
Untitled Landscape #2 1994

Acrylic on canvas, 272.5 × 304.5
Inscribed verso BR: *Untitled Landscape
#2 Dominic Denis 1994*
Purchased from Anthony Wilkinson
Fine Art December 1994
P6290

Durward Graham B 1956
America, does it Exist? 1985

Oil on canvas, 183.5 × 168
Inscribed verso TRC: *AMERICA DOES IT EXIST*
Purchased from 369 Gallery, Edinburgh November 1986
P5433

Farthing Stephen B 1950
Traditional Cover 1985

Oil and wax on canvas, 123 × 107
Inscribed verso TLC: *TRADITIONAL COVER*
Purchased from Edward Totah Gallery May 1986
P5380

Goldsworthy Andy B 1956
Sweet chestnut leaf horn 1987

Sweet chestnut leaves fastened with thorns, 20 × 26 × 10
Purchased from Fabian Carlsson Gallery July 1987
P5502

Gormley Antony B 1950
Out of this World 1983–84

Lead on a fibreglass carcass lined with unfired clay, with a fired clay figure resting on top
Head: 80 × 120 × 90
Figure: 50 × 40 × 30
Overall size: 130 × 120 × 90
Purchased from Riverside Studios October 1984
P4961 (colour plate 11)

Fairhurst Angus B 1966
Ultramarine Attachment (Laura Loves Fish) 1992

Cibachrome, mounted on MDF board, garment attachments – Edition 2/2
175 × 120
Purchased from Serpentine Gallery May 1994
P6269 (colour plate 9)

Finer Stephen B 1949
Woman of Thirty Seven 1980–82

Oil on canvas, 35.5 × 30.5
Inscribed verso: *SA Finer 1980–82*
Purchased from Anthony Reynolds Gallery July 1986
P5391

Gordon Douglas B 1966
"10 ms⁻¹" 1994

Video installation on laser disc – one of an edition of three
Purchased from Lisson Gallery December 1994
P6292 (colour plate 10)

Gouk Alan B 1939
Eyelash Swoop 1985–87

Oil on canvas, 116.8 × 147.3
Inscribed verso T (towards right): *EYELASH SWOOP*; verso TRC: *Shown Angela Flowers July 87*; verso (towards top and towards right): *85 – 85 Alan Gouk;* verso R (above centre): *Alan Gouk Sept – Oct '85 – Jan '87*; verso upper L: *A. Gouk*
Purchased from Angela Flowers Gallery December 1987
P5579 (cover illustration)

Fairnington Mark B 1957
The Rotten Aubergine 1986

Acrylic and collage on paper, 61 × 91
Inscribed BL: *Fairnington '86*
Purchased from the artist February 1989
P5621

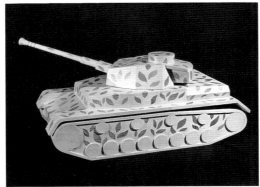

Finlay Ian Hamilton B 1925
Panzer Mk IV: Homage to Poussin 1976

Wood and wood inlay, 26 × 69 × 28
Purchased from the artist October 1985
P5305

CAMOUFLAGE

CAMOUFLAGE IS FIELDS AND STREAMS AND TREES IN IDEAL FORM, WHICH NONE BUT POUSSIN SEES.

Ian Hamilton Finlay

GREEN Alan B 1932
Blue Towards Violet 1985

Oil on canvas, 120 × 120
Inscribed verso TRC: *ALAN GREEN BLUE TOWARDS VIOLET 1985*
Purchased from Juda Rowan Gallery September 1985
P5301

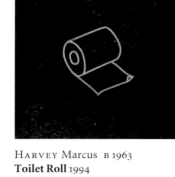

HARVEY Marcus B 1963
Toilet Roll 1994

Oil on canvas, 61 × 61
Purchased from Serpentine Gallery May 1994
P6270 (colour plate 13)

HICKS Nicola B 1960
The Last Leaf Dragon 1986

Charcoal and pastel on paper, 115 × 204
Purchased from Angela Flowers Gallery December 1986
P5449

HODGE Wendy B 1953
Tower of Babel, Docklands 1989

Oil on canvas, 154 × 165
Inscribed verso: *Wendy Hodge Tower of Babel, Docklands*
Purchased from Angela Flowers Gallery July 1990
P5816

HAMILTON Richard B 1922
Testament 1993

Oil on Cibachrome on canvas, 82 × 60
Purchased from Anthony d'Offay Gallery March 1994
P6222 (colour plate 12)

HAYWARD Tony B 1954
Above and Below 1989

Mixed media, 130.6 × 63 × 78.9
Purchased from the artist May 1991
P5927

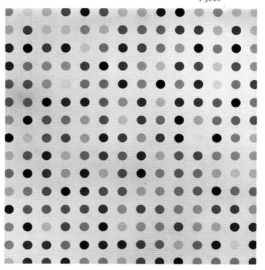

HIRST Damien B 1965
Apotryptophanae 1994

Household gloss and emulsion on canvas, 205.5 × 221
Inscribed on horizontal cross-bar of stretcher centre L: *3 inchspo*; on horizontal cross-bar of stretcher centre R: *Apotryptophanae 3″*
Purchased from Serpentine Gallery May 1994
P6271

HARDIE Gwen B 1962
Breasts II 1986

Oil on paper, 75 × 100
Inscribed verso T: *GWEN HARDIE, "BREASTS II", 75 × 100 cm, Sept 1986*
Purchased from Paton Gallery October 1986
P5425

HEPHER David B 1935
Study 1993

Acrylic, plaster and PVA on canvas 35.9 × 76.3
Inscribed BLC: *WEST HAM*; verso TRC: ③
Purchased from Angela Flowers Gallery November 1994
P6287

HODGE Wendy B 1953
Stepney Farm 1989

Oil on canvas, 51.6 × 110.5
Inscribed verso: *Wendy Hodge Stepney Farm 1989*
Purchased from the artist December 1989
P5743

HOUSHIARY Shirazeh B 1955
The Pen and the Ant 1984

Copper, 185 × 50 × 20
Purchased from Lisson Gallery November 1984
P4962

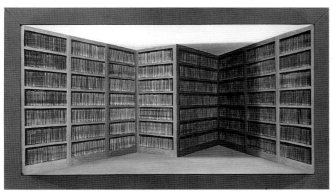

HUGHES Patrick B 1939
Volumes 1992

Oil on board, 96 × 170.5 × 38
Inscribed verso: <u>Volumes</u> Patrick Hughes 1992
Purchased from Angela Flowers Gallery December 1992
P6130

JACKOWSKI Andrzej B 1947
Tower of Copernicus – Spring 1983

Oil on canvas, 147.5 × 132
Inscribed on stretcher: ANDRZEJ JACKOWSKI TOWER OF COPERNICUS – SPRING
Purchased from Anne Berthoud Gallery January 1985
P4994

JEFFRIES Neil B 1959
My Best Friend 1984

Oil on sheet metal, 114.3 × 128.3 × 33
Purchased from Blond Fine Art June 1984
P4883

HUME Gary B 1962
Abandoned 1992

Mixed media on PVC panel with wood veneer, 215.9 × 154.9
Inscribed BLC: <i>Abandoned 1992</i>; verso upper L: <i>HUME 92</i>
Purchased from Karsten Schubert, London August 1992
P6092

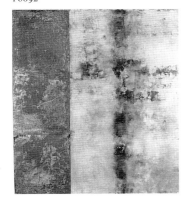

HYND Jonathan B 1950
Inter-Relations 1991

Mixed media on board, 134 × 118
Inscribed verso: <u>Jonathan Hynd</u>
Purchased from the artist April 1993
P6178

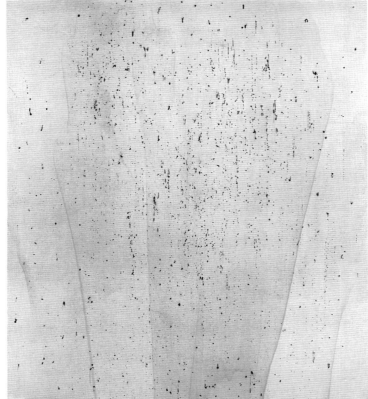

INNES Callum B 1962
Untitled 1992

Oil and shellac on canvas, 220 × 190
Inscribed on horizontal cross-bar of stretcher L: <i>C Innes 92</i>; on horizontal cross-bar of stretcher centre: <i>C Innes 92</i>
Purchased from Frith Street Gallery May 1992
P6063

JONES Lucy B 1955
Big Ben, Trafalgar Square 1991

Oil on canvas, 91.5 × 122
Purchased from Angela Flowers Gallery April 1991
P5926

KINDNESS John B 1951
Doctors and Patience 1990

Taxicab fragment – etched and painted 101.6 × 152.4
Purchased from Kerlin Gallery, Dublin April 1991
P5925

KINLEY Peter 1926–1988
Leaves 1977–78

Oil on canvas, 116.5 × 152.4
Inscribed verso T: *leaves 40 × 60 1977–78
Peter Kinley*
Purchased from Catherine Kinley, the
artist's widow, March 1992
P6046

KNEALE Bryan B 1930
Cat 1986

Conté chalk on paper, 110 × 82
Inscribed BRC: *Bryan Kneale 86*
Purchased from the artist December
1986
P5450

KOSSOFF Leon B 1926
Head of Chaim 1985

Charcoal and pastel on paper, 79.2 × 56
Purchased from Anthony d'Offay
Gallery May 1993
P6181

KRUT Ansel B 1959
Woman with Monkey 1985

Oil on canvas, 176 × 118
Inscribed verso: *A. KRUT 1985
c/o RCA "Woman with monkey"
VIENNA, KUNSTLERHAUS*
Purchased from Fischer Fine Art
July 1986
P5408

KINLEY Peter 1926–1988
Turtle with Towers 1984

Oil on canvas, 76.2 × 101.6
Inscribed verso T: *Peter Kinley. Turtle
with Towers 30 × 40 1984*
Purchased from the artist February 1985
P5000

KONDRACKI Henry B 1953
On the Road Alone 1989

Oil on canvas, 137 × 122
Inscribed BRC: *KONDRACKI*
Purchased from Vanessa Devereux
Gallery November 1989
P5749

KITAJ R B B 1932
Melancholy after Dürer 1989

Oil on canvas, 123.5 × 122.5
Inscribed verso TLC: *MELANCHOLY
AFTER DÜRER 1989 Kitaj*
Purchased from Marlborough Fine Art
March 1990
P5803 (colour plate 14)

KOSSOFF Leon B 1926
Head of Rosalind 1981

Oil on board, 51.5 × 46.5
Purchased at Christie's through
Anthony d'Offay Gallery December
1993
P6209 (colour plate 15)

KOSSOFF Leon B 1926
Christchurch Spitalfields, Spring
1987

Oil on board, 61.5 × 56
Purchased from Anthony d'Offay
Gallery October 1988
P5612

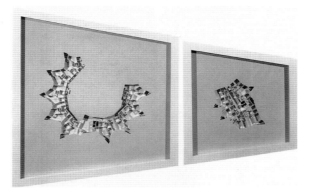

LANDY Michael B 1963
I'm Forever Blowing Bubbles (small) No. 2 1991

Wood, steel and gloss paint
Diameter 40.6
Purchased from Karsten Schubert,
London March 1992
P6056

LANGLANDS & BELL
LANGLANDS Ben B 1955
BELL Nikki B 1959
Romeo & Julia (diptych) 1990

Poplar, MDF, wood products, glass and
AC lacquer
Left panel: 96 × 86 × 15
Right panel: 68 × 59 × 15
Overall size: 96 × 151 × 15
Left panel inscribed verso B: ROMEO &
JULIA (JULIA) Langlands & Bell 1990;
right panel inscribed verso B: ROMEO &
JULIA (ROMEO) Langlands & Bell 1990
Purchased from the artists August 1992
P6090

LESSORE John B 1939
Artist and Model III 1988

Oil on board, 91 × 122.5
Purchased from Nigel Greenwood
Gallery October 1989
P5648

LANE Abigail B 1967
(Ann Elliott)* 1992

Two objects: Ann Elliott's footprint cast
in rubber on the base of each object –
one of 20 custom-made pairs; with
presentation box
Wood, rubber and metal tacks
Each object: 12.8 × 10.3 × 25.1
Overall size as installed
Purchased from Karsten Schubert,
London December 1992
P6129
*Ann Elliott is a former Exhibition
Officer of the British Council's Visual
Arts Department

LAW Bob B 1934
Don't Take My Heart Away 1987

Bronze (in two parts)
Coffin: 3.4 × 6.6 × 19
Heart: 7.7 × 5.8 × 2.5
Overall size: 6.7 × 7.5 × 19
Stamped inside coffin: DONT TAKE MY
HEART AWAY 07
Purchased from the artist April 1988
P5588

LEAPMAN David B 1959
Decoy 1992

Dayglo and interference acrylic on
canvas, 175 × 215
Purchased from Todd Gallery
September 1992
P6095 (colour plate 16)

LE BRUN Christopher B 1951
Heartland 1986

Oil on canvas, 178 × 167
Inscribed verso upper L: 12.2.86 → 11.86;
verso upper R: HEARTLAND Christopher
Le Brun
Purchased from Nigel Greenwood
Gallery November 1986
P5446

LEWIS Tim B 1961
Arrogance of Coherence 1987

Bronze, 11.5 × 20.5 × 5.7
Purchased from Angela Flowers Gallery
July 1987
P5509

LEWIS Tim B 1961
Angel 1989

Steel, wood and electric motor
94.5 × 41 × 41
Purchased from Angela Flowers Gallery
November 1989
P5711

LONG Richard B 1945
Three Moors Three Circles 1982

Framed work: text, 106.1 × 164
Purchased from Anthony d'Offay
Gallery December 1988
P5620

LEWIS Tim B 1961
Arrogance of Coherence 1987

Felt pen, shellac and acrylic on paper
83.5 × 118
Purchased from Angela Flowers Gallery
July 1987
P5510

LEWIS Tim B 1961
Conceit of Retention 1994

Mixed media installation: fibreglass,
acrylic paint, steel, two electric motors,
two light stands, strobe and spotlights,
timer switch, and cabling
Dimensions variable: overall size as
installed
Purchased from Angela Flowers Gallery
July 1994
P6283

LONG Richard B 1945
Spring Circle 1992

Delabole slate, Diameter 300
Purchased from Anthony d'Offay
Gallery July 1994
P6284 (colour plate 17)

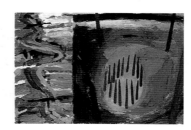

LEWIS Tim B 1961
Arrogance of Coherence 1987

Felt pen, shellac and acrylic on paper
83.5 × 118
Purchased from Angela Flowers Gallery
July 1987
P5511

LOKER John B 1938
By Pass 1985

Oil on paper, 50.5 × 76
Inscribed BLC: '*By Pass*'; BRC: *John
Loker/85*
Purchased from Angela Flowers Gallery
May 1985
P5300

MCFADYEN Jock B 1950
Even Dwarves . . . 1987

Oil on canvas, 198.2 × 134.5
Purchased from the artist September
1987
P5563

McFadyen Jock B 1950
Canal 1991

Gouache on paper, 76.2 × 57.2
Inscribed BR: *'Canal' Jock McFadyen '91*
Purchased from William Jackson
Gallery June 1992
P6077

McFadyen Jock B 1950
Canary 1991

Gouache on paper, 76.2 × 57.2
Inscribed B centre: *Canary*; BRC: *Jock McFadyen '91*
Purchased from William Jackson
Gallery June 1992
P6078 (colour plate 18)

Mach David B 1956
Golden Oldie 1992

Mixed media comprising AIWA audio
system (radio and tape deck), AIWA
turntable with 96 vinyl LP records, and
fibreglass figure with two speakers
AIWA audio system (radio and tape
deck): 25.7 × 36 × 35.5
AIWA turntable with 96 vinyl LP records:
27.2 × 49 × 39
Fibreglass figure with two speakers:
82.7 × 86.2 × 88.2
Overall size: 108.6 × 109.8 × 96
Purchased from the artist May 1992
P6096 (colour plate 19)

McKeever Ian B 1946
Thicket 1984

Collage and oil on photograph on
canvas, 221 × 228.6
Inscribed verso: *THICKET 1984 Collage
&c Oil on Photograph on canvas. 87″ ×
90″ Collection: The Artist*
Purchased from Nigel Greenwood
Gallery February 1985
P4999

McKenna Stephen B 1939
The Evidence 1985

Oil on canvas, 100 × 75
Inscribed verso TL: K8512
Stephen McKenna 1985; and on all four
edges of verso frame: *K8512*
Purchased from Edward Totah Gallery
October 1985
P5304

McLean John B 1939
Buff Bay 1993

Acrylic on canvas, 78.1 × 129.5
Inscribed verso T: *"BUFF BAY" John
McLean 1993;* and on stretcher: © *John
McLean "BUFF BAY", A/C 1993*
Purchased from Francis Graham-Dixon
Gallery March 1994
P6223 (colour plate 20)

McGinn Martin B 1955
Untitled (Divided Filter) 1990

Galvanised wire mesh (diptych)
Left panel: 86.1 × 81.2 × 5.5
Right panel: 86.1 × 81.2 × 5.5
Overall size: 86.1 × 162.4 × 5.5
Left panel inscribed verso upper L: *LEFT
PANEL 63¼ X 34 X 2¼;* right panel
inscribed verso upper L: *RIGHT PANEL
63¼ X 34 X 2¼*
Purchased from Curwen Gallery
January 1991
P5852

McLean John B 1939
Corbie 1993

Acrylic on canvas, 61.3 × 188.3
Inscribed verso R: *"CORBIE" 1993 John
McLean*
Purchased from Francis Graham-Dixon
Gallery March 1994
P6224

MAGILL Elizabeth B 1959
Hop, One, Two, One Two Three Four 1991

Oil on scanned canvas, 183 × 244.2
Inscribed verso L (above centre): '*hop 1, 2*' MAGILL '91 *oil on* SCANNED CANVAS
Purchased from Kerlin Gallery, Dublin December 1991
P6004

MILROY Lisa B 1959
Miso 1991

Monotype, 30 × 38.1
Inscribed BLC: '*Miso*'; BRC: *Lisa Milroy 1991*
Presented by the artist August 1991
P5961

MISTRY Dhruva B 1957
Seated Figure 3 1988

Ink and gouache on paper, 31 × 23
Inscribed BRC: *D Mistry 1988*; verso B: '*Seated figure – 3*' 1988 *Ink and gouache D Mistry*
Purchased from the artist March 1994
P6319

MISTRY Dhruva B 1957
Seated Figure 4 1988

Ink and gouache on paper, 31 × 23
Inscribed BRC: *D Mistry 1988*; verso B: '*Seated figure 4*' 1988 *ink and gouache D Mistry*
Purchased from the artist March 1994
P6320

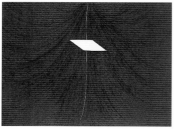

MALINOWSKI Antoni B 1955
Not Titled 1990

Acrylic on canvas, 183 × 244
Inscribed TR on top turnover of canvas: *ANTONI MALINOWSKI NO TITLE 1990*
Purchased from the artist February 1991
P5876

MILROY Lisa B 1959
Sushi 1991

Monotype, 24.7 × 39.2
Inscribed BLC: '*Sushi*'; BRC: *Lisa Milroy 1991*
Presented by the artist August 1991
P5962

MISTRY Dhruva B 1957
Tree Spirit 1 1988–90

Bronze – Edition 1/5, 58.7 × 28.5 × 25 (with base)
Purchased from Nigel Greenwood Gallery March 1992
P6047

MILROY Lisa B 1959
Stamps 1986

Oil on canvas, 189.2 × 198.1
Purchased from Nicola Jacobs Gallery June 1986
P5409 (colour plate 21)

MISTRY Dhruva B 1957
White Elephant 1987

Bronze – one of an edition of five
29 × 42 × 16
Purchased from Nigel Greenwood Gallery December 1987
P5580

MISTRY Dhruva B 1957
Hanuman: Study for a Spatial Metaphor 1988–93

Plaster, enamel paint and shellac
30.3 × 30.3 × 2.6
Incised verso centre: *D Mistry 1988*;
inscribed verso centre: *FOR TRUPTI 2 OCT 1993*; verso lower L: *'1988–'93'*; verso B: *Hanuman: Study for a Spatial Metaphor*
Purchased from the artist March 1994
P6316

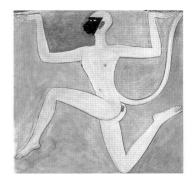

MISTRY Dhruva B 1957
Hanuman: Study for a Spatial Metaphor 1993

Watercolour, crayon and acrylic on paper, 75 × 75
Inscribed verso B: *Hanuman: Study for a Spatial Metaphor 1993 Watercolour, crayon, acrylic*
Purchased from the artist March 1994
P6321

MOORE Henry 1898–1986
Helmet Head No. 6 1975

Bronze – Edition of 9+1
Height 44, diameter 55.5 (with base)
Inscribed on base: *Moore*; stamped on base: *4/9*
Acquired by exchange with the Henry Moore Foundation September 1989
P6083

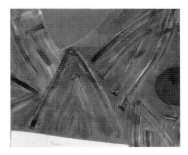

MORRIS Mali B 1945
Dumela Mma 1991–92

Acrylic on canvas, 141 × 165.1
Inscribed verso upper R: © *Mali Morris DUMELA MMA 1991–2*; on stretcher T centre: *DUMELA MMA*; on stretcher TR: *MALI MORRIS 91-2*; on centre bar of stretcher: *MALI MORRIS*
Purchased from Francis Graham-Dixon Gallery April 1992
P6058

MISTRY Dhruva B 1957
Light, Passion and Darkness 5 1992–93

Plaster and gold leaf, 30.2 × 31 × 2
Incised verso centre: *D Mistry 1992–1993.*; inscribed verso B: *"Light, Passion and Darkness. 5"* 1992–93 *Plaster and Goldleaf Dhruva Mistry*
Purchased from the artist March 1994
P6317 (colour plate 22)

MOORE Henry 1898–1986
Composition 1934

Bronze – Edition of 9+2, cast in 1961 from the original in reinforced concrete
19.8 × 42.5 × 20 (with base)
Inscribed on underside of base: *Moore*; stamped on base: *0/9*
Acquired by exchange with the Henry Moore Foundation September 1989
P6081

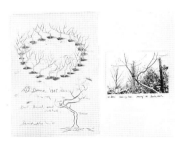

NASH David B 1945
Ash Dome 1985

(continued documentation of **Fletched over Ash Dome**, planted 1977 at Caen-y-Coed, Gwynedd)
Mixed media drawing and black and white photograph
Drawing: 57 × 39.5
Photograph: 22.6 × 29
Drawing inscribed centre L: *Ash Dome 1985*; lower L: *Bent, Pruned, and mulched.*; BL: *David Nash '85*
Photograph inscribed BE: *'Ash Dome'. Caen-y-Coed. 'pruning'. 1985 David Nash*
Purchased from the artist April 1985
P5299

MISTRY Dhruva B 1957
Light, Passion and Darkness 11 1992–93

Plaster and gold leaf, 30.7 × 31.1 × 2
Incised verso centre: *D Mistry 1992–1993*; inscribed verso B: *"Light, Passion and Darkness. – 11"* 1992–93 *Plaster and Goldleaf Dhruva Mistry*
Purchased from the artist March 1994
P6318

MOORE Henry 1898–1986
Maquette for Fallen Warrior 1956

Bronze – Edition of 10+1
13.5 × 26.5 × 15.3 (with base)
Acquired by exchange with the Henry Moore Foundation September 1989
P6082

MOORE Henry 1898–1986
Maquette for Mother and Child: Upright 1977

Bronze – Edition of 9+2, 22 × 11.5 × 10 (with base)
Inscribed on base: *Moore*; stamped on base: *0/9*
Acquired by exchange with the Henry Moore Foundation September 1989
P6084

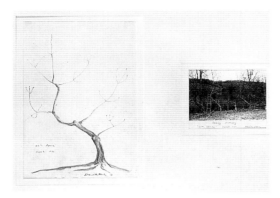

Nash David B 1945
Ash Dome 1987

(continued documentation of
Fletched over Ash Dome, planted 1977
at Caen-y-Coed, Gwynedd)
Pencil on paper and black and white
photograph
Drawing: 59.2 × 42
Photograph: 21.9 × 28.2
Drawing inscribed L: *'ash dome'*
March 1987; BR: *David Nash '87*
Photograph inscribed B centre: *heavy*
pruning; BE: *'ash Dome' March 1987*
David Nash
Purchased from the artist November
1987
P5577

Nash David B 1945
One Tree of the Ash Dome 1991

(continued documentation of
Fletched over Ash Dome, planted 1977
at Caen-y-Coed, Gwynedd)
Charcoal on paper and black and white
photograph
Drawing: 70.4 × 50.1
Photograph: 20 × 28.5
Drawing inscribed lower L: *one tree of*
the Ash Dome 1991 David Nash
Photograph inscribed BL: *Ash Dome*
March 1991; B: *David Nash*
Purchased from the artist September
1991
P5967

Newman Avis B 1946
Study for Reptile (No. 2) 1987

Charcoal on paper, 100 × 137.5
Purchased from Lisson Gallery January
1988
P5581

Ofili Chris B 1968
Painting with Shit on it 1993

Acrylic and oil paint, polyester resin
and pigment, and elephant dung on
linen, resting on two elephant dung
supports, 182.5 × 123
Left support: height 12; right support:
height 8.5
Purchased from Anthony Wilkinson
Fine Art December 1994
P6289 (colour plate 23)

Olivant David B 1958
Untitled 1989-90

Compressed charcoal on paper
192 × 161
Purchased from the artist January 1990
P6007

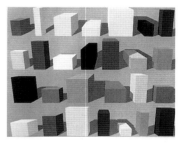

Opie Julian B 1958
Imagine you can order these (1)
1992

Acrylic on wood, glass and aluminium
128.5 × 158.8 × 6
Purchased from Lisson Gallery August
1992
P6091 (colour plate 24)

Oulton Thérèse B 1953
Mortal Coil 1984

Oil on canvas, 234 × 213
Inscribed verso TRC: *Thérèse Oulton*
Mortal Coil '84
Purchased from Gimpel Fils August
1984
P4904

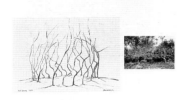

Nash David B 1945
Ash Dome 1989

(continued documentation of
Fletched over Ash Dome, planted 1977
at Caen-y-Coed, Gwynedd)
Charcoal on paper and black and white
photograph
Drawing: 50.1 × 70.4
Photograph: 20 × 28.5
Drawing inscribed BLC: *Ash Dome 1989*;
BRC: *David Nash*
Photograph inscribed BL: *Ash Dome*
August 1989; BR: *David Nash*
Purchased from the artist September
1991
P5966

Nash David B 1945
Ash Dome (update) 1993

(continued documentation of
Fletched over Ash Dome, planted 1977
at Caen-y-Coed, Gwynedd)
Charcoal, pastel and pencil on paper
and black and white photograph
Drawing: 76.2 × 56
Photograph: 30.5 × 20.5
Drawing inscribed BL: *Ash Dome*
(update) 93; BR: *David Nash '93*
Photograph inscribed BL: *Ash Dome*
update 1993; BR: *David Nash*
Purchased from the artist December
1994
P6322

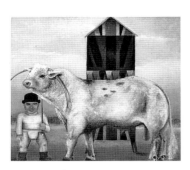

PARKER Alan B 1965
There's No Show Without Punch
1992

Oil on canvas, 122 × 137.5
Inscribed verso TR: *Alan Parker '92*
"THERE'S NO SHOW WITHOUT PUNCH"
Purchased from the Sussex Open 1993
October 1993
P6196

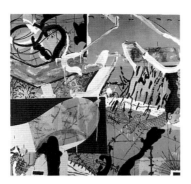

RAE Fiona B 1963
Untitled (green, blue and black)
1992

Oil on canvas, 182.9 × 182.9
Inscribed centre on top turnover of
canvas: *Fiona Rae 1992 Untitled (green,*
blue and black)
Purchased from Waddington Galleries
January 1993
P6131

REGO Paula B 1935
Untitled 'Girl and Dog' series 1986

Acrylic on paper, 112 × 76
Purchased from Edward Totah Gallery
March 1987
P5484

PARKER Cornelia B 1956
Falling 1990

Silver plated trophies and dish-wire
81.3 × 17.8
Purchased from the Contemporary Art
Society Market October 1990
P5835

RANDALL-PAGE Peter B 1954
Untitled 1985

Charcoal on paper, 76.2 × 56.7
Inscribed BRC: Artist's monogram '85
Purchased from the Contemporary Art
Society Market November 1986
P5447

RAE Fiona B 1963
Untitled (purple and yellow I) 1991

Oil and charcoal on canvas, 198.1 × 213.4
Inscribed centre L on top turnover of
canvas: *Fiona Rae Untitled (purple &*
yellow I) 1991
Purchased from Waddington Galleries
July 1991
P5960

RANDALL-PAGE Peter B 1954
Untitled 1985

Charcoal on paper, 76.2 × 56.7
Inscribed BRC: Artist's monogram '85
Purchased from the Contemporary Art
Society Market November 1986
P5448

REGO Paula B 1935
Snare 1987

Acrylic on paper mounted on canvas
150 × 150
Purchased from Edward Totah Gallery
March 1987
P5485 (colour plate 25)

ROBERTS John B 1947
No. 14 Drawing from City series
1984

Charcoal on paper, 142.2 × 104.1
Inscribed BR: *R 84*
Purchased from the artist February
1985
P5001

SALTER Rebecca B 1955
Untitled (grey) 1984
Mixed media monoprint (woodblock)
47 × 63.5
Inscribed BRC: *Rebecca Salter*
Purchased from Curwen Gallery
February 1985
P5006

SMITH Keir B 1950
Kentish Fire 1984
Rusted iron on paper, 137.2 × 101.7
Purchased from the artist January 1985
P4996

STUBBS Michael B 1961
Untitled 1990
Oil on stacked canvases, 31 × 30.5 × 18.5
Purchased from the 1990 Whitechapel
Open January 1991
P5846

SUTTON Trevor B 1948
Joseph 1990
Oil on board, 38.2 × 38
Inscribed verso T: *JOSEPH. 1990. TREVOR
SUTTON. 8″ to CENTRES*; verso BR:
Trevor Sutton.
Purchased from the artist November
1992
P6120

SALTER Rebecca B 1955
Untitled (purple/red) 1984
Mixed media monoprint (woodblock)
50.2 × 72.4
Inscribed BRC: *Rebecca Salter*
Purchased from Curwen Gallery
February 1985
P5007

STAHL Andrew B 1954
Bird and Fountain 1985
Oil on canvas, 152.5 × 121.9
Inscribed verso R: *STAHL BIRD AND
FOUNTAIN*
Purchased from the artist March 1985
P5053

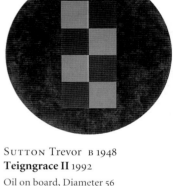

SUTTON Trevor B 1948
Teigngrace II 1992
Oil on board, Diameter 56
Inscribed verso T: *TEIGNGRACE. II. 1992.
TREVOR SUTTON.*; verso BR: *Trevor
Sutton.*
Purchased from the artist November
1992
P6119 (colour plate 26)

SUTTON Trevor B 1948
Thinking South 1993
Oil on board, Diameter 94
Inscribed verso centre: *THINKING
SOUTH. 1993. TREVOR SUTTON.*; verso BR:
Trevor Sutton.
Purchased from Smith.Jariwala Gallery
February 1994
P6210

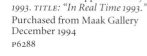

SMITH Dillwyn B 1958
In Real Time 1993 1993
Acrylic on cotton, 228.4 × 167.8
Inscribed verso upper R: *Dillwyn Smith
1993. TITLE: "In Real Time 1993."*
Purchased from Maak Gallery
December 1994
P6288

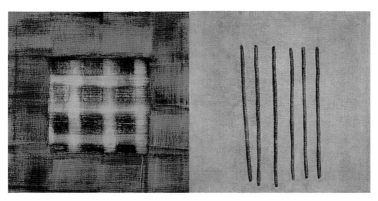

THOMPSON Estelle B 1960
Diptych No. 1 (Untitled) 1990

Oil on linen
Left panel: 61 × 61
Right panel: 61 × 61
Overall size: 61 × 122
Left panel inscribed verso BRC: *Estelle Thompson 1990*; right panel inscribed verso BRC: *Estelle Thompson 1990*
Purchased from Pomeroy Purdy Gallery February 1991
P5853

TREISTER Suzanne B 1958
Blood Cells Video Game 1989

Oil on canvas, 51 × 40.5
Inscribed verso: '"*BLOOD CELLS*" – *VIDEO GAME*' *SUZANNE TREISTER 1989*
Purchased from Edward Totah Gallery October 1989
P5650

WEBB Boyd B 1947
Tethered Ray 1981

Unique colour photograph, 98 × 71.5
Inscribed verso: *Tethered Ray 1981 Boyd Webb Cat. No. 080.0*
Purchased from Anthony d'Offay Gallery January 1987
P5474

TREISTER Suzanne B 1958
Model Kit No. 3 1989

Oil on canvas, 213.5 × 183
Inscribed verso upper R: *SUZANNE TREISTER MODEL KIT (No. 3)*; verso upper L: *TOP* ↑
Purchased from Edward Totah Gallery October 1989
P5649

TURNBULL Alison B 1956
Alcazaba 1988

Oil on canvas, 149.9 × 199.1
Purchased from Anne Berthoud Gallery December 1989
P5726

WALLINGER Mark B 1959
The Bottom Line 1986

Oil on board, 122 × 99.5
Inscribed verso centre L: *THE BOTTOM LINE*
Purchased from Anthony Reynolds Gallery February 1987
P5482 (colour plate 27)

WEBB Boyd B 1947
Corral 1989

Unique colour photograph, 158 × 123
Inscribed verso: *Corral 1989 Boyd Webb Cat. No. 0249*
Purchased from Anthony d'Offay Gallery November 1989
P5725

WEBB Boyd B 1947
Whelp 1990

Unique colour photograph (diptych – panels framed separately)
Each panel: 158 × 123
Left panel inscribed verso: *Whelp 1990 Boyd Webb Cat. No. 0272*; right panel inscribed verso: *Whelp 1990 Boyd Webb Cat. No. 0273*
Purchased from Anthony d'Offay Gallery October 1991
P5976 (colour plate 28)

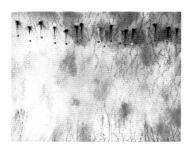

WEBB Boyd B 1947
Ebb 1993

Unique colour photograph, 123 × 158
Inscribed verso: *Ebb 1993 Boyd Webb Cat. No. 0308*
Purchased from Anthony d'Offay Gallery February 1994
P6226

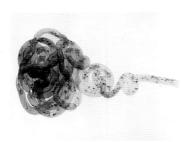

WEBB Boyd B 1947
Donor 1994

Unique colour photograph, 123 × 158
Inscribed verso: *Donor 1994 Boyd Webb Cat. No. 0318*
Purchased from Anthony d'Offay Gallery February 1994
P6225

WHITEFORD Kate B 1952
Symbol Stone 1983

From **Symbol Stone** series
Oil on paper, 152 × 114
Purchased from the artist October 1986
P5422

WHITEFORD Kate B 1952
Symbol Stone 1983

From **Symbol Stone** series
Oil on paper, 152 × 114
Purchased from the artist October 1986
P5420

WHITEFORD Kate B 1952
Symbol Stone 1983

From **Symbol Stone** series
Oil on paper, 152 × 114
Purchased from the artist October 1986
P5421

WHITEFORD Kate B 1952
Symbol Stone 1983

From **Symbol Stone** series
Oil on paper, 152 × 114
Purchased from the artist October 1986
P5423

WHITEREAD Rachel B 1963
False Door 1990

Plaster, 214.6 × 152.4 × 40.6
Purchased from Karsten Schubert, London April 1991
P5919 (colour plate 29)

WILDING Alison B 1948
Nature: Blue and Gold 1984

Brass, oil and pigment on ash
47 × 103 × 22
Purchased from Salvatore Ala Gallery, Milan March 1985
P5055 (colour plate 30)

WILDING Alison B 1948
Veiled 1991–93

Acrylic and basalt resin (four objects, displayed in two parts)
Left part: 40 × 20.4 × 21
Right part: 39.3 × 20.5 × 20.3
Overall size as installed
Purchased from Karsten Schubert, London July 1993
P6127

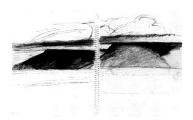

WILKINSON Donald B 1937
Cloud Sequence: Rhum 1979

Conté crayon and charcoal on paper
Two sheets: each 25.2 × 20.2
Overall size: 25.2 × 40.5
Left sheet inscribed BLC: ② *11.10*; right
sheet BLC: *2*
Purchased from the artist November
1984
P4981A

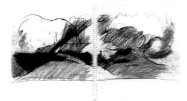

WILKINSON Donald B 1937
Cloud Sequence: Rhum 1979

Conté crayon and charcoal on paper
Two sheets: each 25.2 × 20.2
Overall size: 25.2 × 40.5
Left sheet inscribed BLC: *5*; right sheet
BLC: *5*
Purchased from the artist November
1984
P4981D

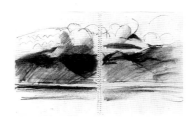

WILKINSON Donald B 1937
Cloud Sequence: Rhum 1979

Conté crayon and charcoal on paper
Two sheets: each 25.2 × 20.2
Overall size: 25.2 × 40.5
Left sheet inscribed BLC: *8.*; right sheet
BLC: *8*
Purchased from the artist November
1984
P4981G

WINSTANLEY Paul B 1954
Landscape 6 1993

Oil on canvas, 175 × 222.2
Inscribed verso TLC: *WINSTANLEY.
Landscape 6. 1993.*
Purchased from Maureen Paley/Interim
Art May 1994
P6273

WILKINSON Donald B 1937
Cloud Sequence: Rhum 1979

Conté crayon and charcoal on paper
Two sheets: each 25.2 × 20.2
Overall size: 25.2 × 40.5
Left sheet inscribed BLC: *3*; right sheet
BLC: *3*
Purchased from the artist November
1984
P4981B

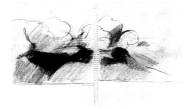

WILKINSON Donald B 1937
Cloud Sequence: Rhum 1979

Conté crayon and charcoal on paper
Two sheets: each 25.2 × 20.2
Overall size: 25.2 × 40.5
Left sheet inscribed BLC: *6.*; right sheet
BLC: *6*
Purchased from the artist November
1984
P4981E

WILKINSON Donald B 1937
Cloud Sequence: Rhum 1979

Conté crayon and charcoal on paper
Two sheets: each 25.2 × 20.2
Overall size: 25.2 × 40.5
Left sheet inscribed BLC: *9.*; right sheet
BLC: *9*
Purchased from the artist November
1984
P4981H

WISZNIEWSKI Adrian B 1958
Culture-Vulturing City Slickers
1986

Pastel on paper, 207.5 × 150
Inscribed TLC: *a wiszniewski*
Purchased from Nigel Greenwood
Gallery October 1986
P5428

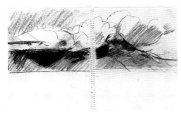

WILKINSON Donald B 1937
Cloud Sequence: Rhum 1979

Conté crayon and charcoal on paper
Two sheets: each 25.2 × 20.2
Overall size: 25.2 × 40.5
Left sheet inscribed BLC: *4*; right sheet
BLC: *4*
Purchased from the artist November
1984
P4981C

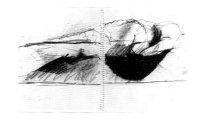

WILKINSON Donald B 1937
Cloud Sequence: Rhum 1979

Conté crayon and charcoal on paper
Two sheets: each 25.2 × 20.2
Overall size: 25.2 × 40.5
Left sheet inscribed BLC: *7.*; right sheet
BLC: *7*
Purchased from the artist November
1984
P4981F

WILLING Victor 1928–1988
23.1.85 1985

Charcoal and pastel on paper
37.2 × 48.7
Inscribed BL: *23.84 23.1.85*
Purchased from Bernard Jacobson
Gallery July 1986
P5407

Wonnacott John B 1940
**Chalkwell Beach, Floodwater
Overflow, Late Afternoon** 1989–92

Oil on board, 61 × 122
Inscribed verso upper L: *John
Wonnacott 1992*
Purchased from Agnew's October 1992
P6111

Woodrow Bill B 1948
Point of Entry 1989

Cardboard into bronze
35.7 × 299.2 × 110.6
Purchased from Lisson Gallery
February 1990
P5769

Yhap Laetitia B 1941
The Steel Boat (Father & Son)
1987–88

Oil on board, 120 × 184 (irregular)
Inscribed verso with a title and
additional information crossed out, but
the following untouched:
*THE STEEL BOAT FATHER & SON 1987–88
Laetitia Yhap 47″ × 72 ½″
120cm × 184cm oil paint*
Purchased from the artist January 1991
P5845

Yhap Laetitia B 1941
**Talking, Laughing and Throwing
Stones** 1991

Oil on gesso on copper, with synthetic
rope, 24 × 48 (semi-circular)
Inscribed verso: *Talking, Laughing and
Throwing Stones Oil on gesso Laetitia
Yhap 24cm × 48cm 1991. Rope is
synthetic primed with Unibond*
Purchased from the artist June 1991
P5963

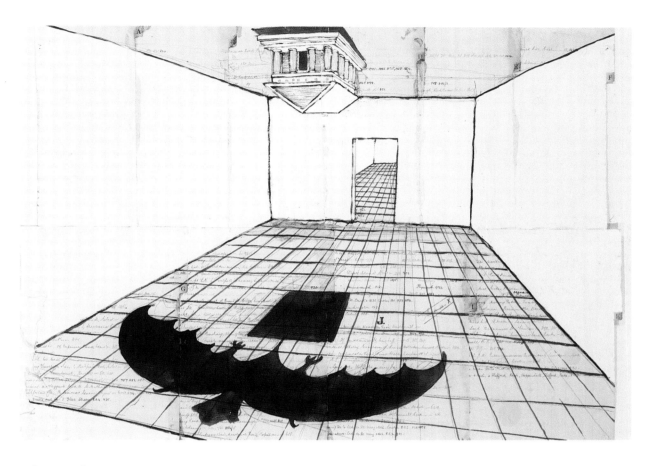

1 EDWARD ALLINGTON
The Daughters of the Night
1982
P6097

2 MICHAEL ANDREWS
**Recollection of a Moment in
October 1989 – The Tobasnich
Burn, Glenartney** 1992
P6132

3 TERRY ATKINSON
Art for the Bunker 7: Bunker in Armagh 11: Ancient Gaelic Ghost after completing a Tour of Duty passing through an Ideological Decontamination Shower before going off duty. Note the Easter Cactus (left) and Easter Lilies and how brightly the Candles continue to burn 1985
P5508

4 FRANK AUERBACH
Tree on Primrose Hill 1984–85
P5359

5 SONIA BOYCE
Pillowcase 1990
P6008

6 STEVEN CAMPBELL
Painting on a Darwinian Theme
1986
P5483

7 PATRICK CAULFIELD
Selected Grapes 1981
P5025

8 EILEEN COOPER
The Self and the Family 1984
P4905

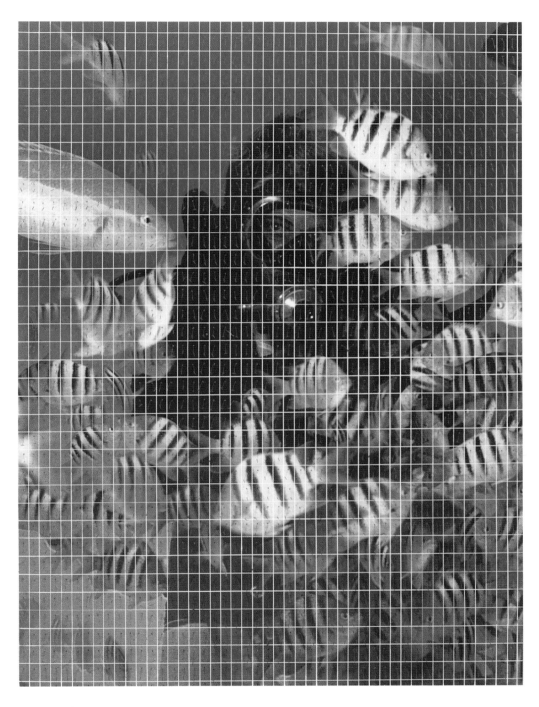

9 ANGUS FAIRHURST
**Ultramarine Attachment
(Laura Loves Fish)** 1992
P6269

10 Douglas Gordon
"10 ms^{-1}" 1994
P6292

11 ANTONY GORMLEY
Out of this World 1983–84
P4961

12 RICHARD HAMILTON
Testament 1993
P6222

13   MARCUS HARVEY
Toilet Roll 1994
P6270

14 R B Kitaj
Melancholy after Dürer 1989
P5803

15 LEON KOSSOFF
Head of Rosalind 1981
P6209

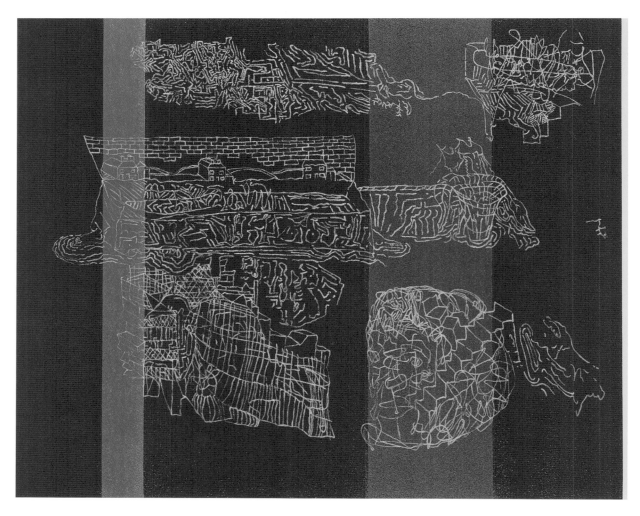

16 DAVID LEAPMAN
Decoy 1992
P6095

17 RICHARD LONG
Spring Circle 1992
P6284

18 JOCK MCFADYEN
Canary 1991
P6078

19 DAVID MACH
Golden Oldie 1992
P6096

20 JOHN MCLEAN
Buff Bay 1993
P6223

21 LISA MILROY
Stamps 1986
P5409

22 DHRUVA MISTRY
Light, Passion and Darkness 5
1992–93
P6317

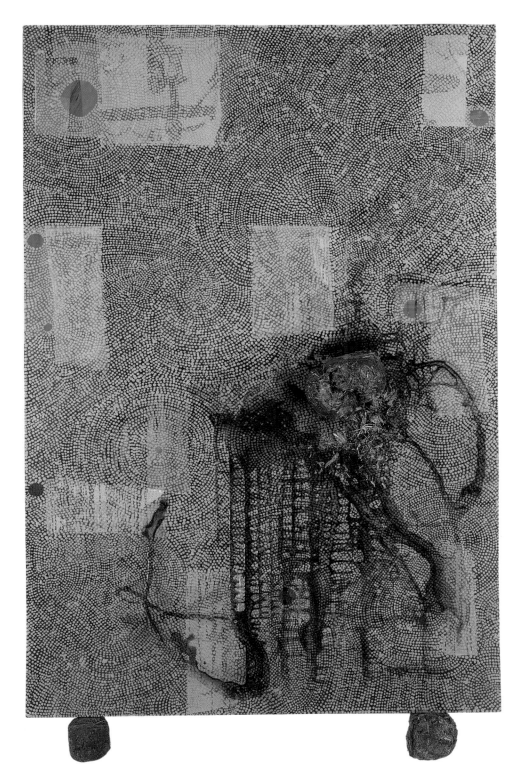

23 CHRIS OFILI
Painting with Shit on it 1993
P6289

24　JULIAN OPIE
Imagine you can order these (1)
1992
P6091

25 PAULA REGO
Snare 1987
P5485

26 TREVOR SUTTON
Teigngrace II 1992
P6119

27 MARK WALLINGER
The Bottom Line 1986
P5482

28 BOYD WEBB
Whelp 1990
P5976

29 RACHEL WHITEREAD
False Door 1990
P5919

30 ALISON WILDING
Nature: Blue and Gold 1984
P5055

31 BILL WOODROW
The Atrium Clock
The British Council, Manchester

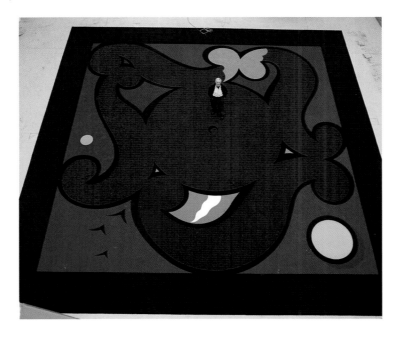

32 PATRICK CAULFIELD
The Atrium Carpet
The British Council, Manchester

33 STEPHEN COX
    Mantra
    The British Council, New Delhi

34 HOWARD HODGKIN
    Facade Mural
    The British Council, New Delhi

PART II : **Commissioned Works**

The British Council is committed to a policy of 'one percent for art', setting aside a percentage of the total building costs specifically for the purchase of works of art for new buildings.

The relocation of a substantial part of the British Council's headquarters operation, from London to Manchester, led in 1991 to two spectacular commissions, one from the sculptor Bill Woodrow for a monumental timepiece, the other from Patrick Caulfield for an atrium carpet. In the same year, Howard Hodgkin and Stephen Cox were commissioned to create works for the British Council's new headquarters in India.

MEDLOCK STREET, MANCHESTER

Patrick Caulfield B 1936
The Atrium Carpet (colour plate 32)

In May 1991 Patrick Caulfield was commissioned to design a carpet for the atrium floor of the British Council's new Northern headquarters. The brief to the artist outlined the concept: "The carpet is intended to make a bold statement about the British Council. We want it in some way to express our role as the principal British agent for overseas cultural relations. We are keener to focus on what we do than on the places we do it."

The finished design, one metre square in acrylic on paper, was delivered in June. Huega (UK) Ltd. – already contracted to supply the main carpeting – were so impressed with it that they undertook to manufacture and install the atrium carpet at their own expense.

It was decided to use synthetic yarn developed by ICI, machine tufted then cut by laser beam. Once the yarns were woven, the artwork was computer scanned. The computer then divided the design into 25 equal sections, each containing 16 carpet tiles, in a proportion that allowed them to fit on the laser bed for cutting. The laser beam, guided by the computer, cut each colour individually – a technique which gives extremely clear definition. Once the cutting was completed, the pieces were re-made into tiles. The finished carpet comprises 2000 tiles and measures 12 × 12 metres.

The following are not reasons for the design but merely associated ideas. The image remains to be interpreted as one will. The overall form of the design has a Celtic-inspired starting-point (i.e. British).

ELEMENTS:
SUN
Source of light/illumination/energy
MOON
Receiver of light/ideas/reception
BIRDS
Travel/messengers/migration
CRESCENT SHADOW
Centre/matrix/source
SMOKE
Signal/message/communication
FOOTPRINT
Human presence/imprint
CARPET OF FLOWERS
Rest/seeds of ideas/artistry
BUTTERFLY FORM
Emergence of ideas
BEE
Cross-fertilisation/industry/symbol of Manchester
CAFÉ
Pause/refreshment/abbreviated signature of artist (i.e. CAulFiEld)
SUMMARY : CONVEYING A MESSAGE
The carpet has a journey; from the footprint clockwise; through the emergence of ideas and on to rest at the carpet of flowers under the moon.

Patrick Caulfield

Bill Woodrow B 1948
The Atrium Clock (colour plate 31)

In March 1991 Bill Woodrow was commissioned to design a clock for the south wall of the atrium. The wall itself measures 25 metres from the floor plate to the spring of the barrel-vaulted roof, and 20 metres across.

The timepiece comprises a central gold disc, flanked on either side by columns. Each column is made up of two halves, each half consisting of three 'faces', mounted on prisms, timed to revolve at twenty minute intervals. The photographer, Jerry Young, was commissioned by Bill Woodrow to take a series of both aerial and ground based landscapes on the theme of world images. The twelve selected landscapes were cut into strips and fixed to the prisms. These photographs revolve in sequence, from top left to top right, lower left to lower right, one changing every five minutes, thus completing the full cycle in the course of an hour.

The clock is 'one handed', the numerals distributed around the upper half only, and the time indicated by the angle created by the upper half as it turns full circle every 24 hours. At noon, the gold circle is complete. At midnight, the upper half is black, the lower half gold. Overall, the clock measures 15.2 metres high by 14 metres wide.

I wanted the clock to provide a contrast to the life of a busy, efficient administrative headquarters by being a source of contemplation about time rather than just an accurate indicator. To this end all obvious movement, which serves to remind us of the inevitability of time passing, has been avoided. There is no minute or second hand, no swinging pendulum, movement of numbers, ticking, bell chiming or things popping in and out on the hour. Movement is reduced to the almost imperceptible solar rotation of the central half-gold, half-black disc and the gentle mesmeric changing of the landscapes flanking it. These landscapes, which display no evidence of human intervention and are supported on classically inspired columns, introduce the possibility of different notions of time, such as memory and imagination, travel and distance, evolution and history. They also act as a reminder of the worldwide community which the British Council serves and of which we are all a part.

Bill Woodrow

Note

The design and maquette for the works by Patrick Caulfield and Bill Woodrow are held by the British Council and are available for study upon request.

Further information on these commissions, and notes on the 96 works of art located in the public areas of the British Council's Northern headquarters, are contained in the catalogue *The British Council Manchester* (ISBN 0 86355 137 8), available from Visual Arts Department.

KASTURBA GANDHI MARG, NEW DELHI

The Indian architect and RIBA gold medallist, Charles Correa, was commissioned to design the building, formally opened at the end of October 1992, which houses the British Council's largest overseas operation. The five-storey building, with interior and exterior spaces flowing into one another through the use of courtyards, pillars and fountains, is designed to reflect a conceptual progression of the history of India.

Stephen Cox B 1946
Mantra (colour plate 33)

This work draws on the great classical tradition of Indian sculpture, but does not make any specific religious reference. It is made of black granite from quarries near the holy city of Kanchipuram, measures 4.9 metres in height, and is 4.3 metres wide and 1.2 metres deep.

The sculpture took over a year to complete, with 20 *shilpies* (carvers) working at Mahabalipuram where Cox has a studio and which was, during the 6th and 7th centuries, the seat of cave temple and Dravidian architecture.

It is visible, through the central doorway, to passers-by from Kasturba Gandhi Marg and constitutes part of the perimeter wall of the building. Looking inward, a massive meditative face emerges from the matrix of the granite, and reflects above a pool, while around it swirl tanmatras*. On the other side, five elements of the tanmatras look down on people passing by the rear of the building.

Its stillness and meditative nature is sympathetic to the work of the edifice to which it is attached - an educational institution, disseminator of ideas, and centre for dialogue.

Stephen Cox

* *Tanmatras* is a term for the relationship between the organs of the senses and the five elements of matter, Earth, Air, Fire, Water and Ether, in Samkhya cosmology.

Howard Hodgkin B 1932
Facade Mural (colour plate 34)

Commissioned by Visual Arts Department to create a new work for the building, Howard Hodgkin collaborated closely with the architect in the production of a magnificent mural for the front facade. The mural is constructed of small, rectangular, hand-cut tiles of white Makrana marble, and black, locally-quarried Cudappah stone – a technique often employed on Mughal buildings.

My first concern was to make a design which would change dramatically when seen from different points of view and thus display the complexity of internal space in the facade of Charles Correa's splendid building.

The moving shadow cast by a large tree seemed an appropriate image for a library and meeting place. I am not a symbolic artist and symbols on buildings often lose their meaning quite quickly but as a symbol a tree is universal and embraces both life and knowledge.

The tree is not of any particular species but I like what one of the contractors said, that the mural shows 'the shadows cast by a giant banyan tree waving in the wind'.

I am delighted with the way the design has been executed by the Indian craftsmen.

Howard Hodgkin

PART III : Graphic Works & Multiples

Entries are arranged by artist in alphabetical order. Where an artist has more than one work in the Collection, the works are given in chronological order. Works of the same year are listed in British Council Collection accession number sequence, unless the actual day or month of completion is known.

1. Name of artist and date of birth (and death).

2. Title of work. Please note that where a complete portfolio appears in an entry, the portfolio title is given first. For single prints from a portfolio, the title of the print is followed by the portfolio title and details. A list of complete mixed portfolios is provided on page 62.

3. Date of work.*

4. Medium.

5. Dimensions are given in centimetres, height preceding width, and image/plate size preceding sheet size. Where the image either fills the entire sheet or lies upon it in such a way that the printed image and paper together form the complete image, no defined image area is given. Dimensions are of the original surface, without mount or frame.

6. Edition number.

7. Source and date of acquisition.

8. British Council Collection accession number.

In this section of the catalogue artists' signatures and inscriptions are not noted.

* The prints which comprise the portfolio **Artists' Choice** were produced 1986/1987. In some cases however the year has not been specified by the artists.

MIXED PORTFOLIOS

Only complete mixed portfolios are listed here. See individual entries under the artists' names.

ARTISTS' CHOICE, a portfolio of 48 prints by 48 artists, published 1987 by the Royal College of Art Printmaking Course in an edition of 48.

Ackroyd, Norman
Allen, Richard
Allen, Susie
Ayres, Gillian
Bellany, John
Berg, Adrian
Bicât, André
Blake, Peter
Blake, Quentin
Buckley, Stephen
Burton, Clive
Caro, Anthony
Collins, Cecil
Culbert, Bill
Davies, Anthony
Denny, Robyn
Dunn, Alf
Edwards, Jeffery
Fielding, Brian
Frink, Elisabeth
Frost, Terry
Golding, John
Grant, Alistair
Heindorff, Michael
Heron, Patrick
Hewitt, John
Hoyland, John
Irvin, Albert
Jacklin, Bill
Jones, Allen
Kiff, Ken
Mara, Tim
Orr, Chris
Paolozzi, Eduardo
Plowman, Chris
Procktor, Patrick
Rego, Paula
Rhodes, Zandra
Rosoman, Leonard
Spear, Ruskin
Stahl, Andrew
Stainton, Tricia
Tilson, Joe
Tindle, David
Trevelyan, Julian
Vaughan, Michael
Weight, Carel
Wentworth, Richard

THE CULFORD PRESS PRINT FOLIO 1988, three prints by three artists, published by Culford Press, London in an edition of 50

Hatt, Christine
Hodes, Charlotte
Stahl, Andrew

LONDON, a portfolio of 11 prints made by 11 artists working in London, published 1992 by Charles Booth-Clibborn under his imprint The Paragon Press in an edition of 65

Denis, Dominic
Fairhurst, Angus
Hirst, Damien
Landy, Michael
Langlands & Bell
May, Nicholas
Quinn, Marc
Taylor, Marcus
Turk, Gavin
Whiteread, Rachel
Wood, Craig

NINE LONDON BIRDS, a portfolio of nine prints by nine artists, published 1994 by the Byam Shaw School of Art in an edition of 80

Ackroyd, Norman
Aitchison, Craigie
Bellany, John
Camp, Jeffery
Caulfield, Patrick
Clough, Prunella
Flanagan, Barry
Hambling, Maggi
Rego, Paula

"OTHER MEN'S FLOWERS", text works by 15 London based artists, curated by Joshua Compston, and published 1994 by Charles Booth-Clibborn under his imprint The Paragon Press in an edition of 100

Bond, Henry
Brisley, Stuart
Brown, Don
Chadwick, Helen
Collishaw, Mat
Doron, Itai
Emin, Tracey
Fairhurst, Angus
Gillick, Liam
Herman, Andrew
Hume, Gary
Staton, Sarah
Taylor-Wood, Sam
Turk, Gavin
Wigram, Max

THE SCOTTISH BESTIARY, 20 prints by seven Scottish artists illustrating the writings in poetry and prose of George Mackay Brown. Published 1986 by Charles Booth-Clibborn under his imprint The Paragon Press in a book edition of 60 and a portfolio edition of 50

Bellany, John
Campbell, Steven
Howson, Peter
Knox, Jack
McLean, Bruce
Redfern, June
Wiszniewski, Adrian

SIX ARTISTS, The 1992 Royal College of Art Portfolio of Prints, published by the Royal College of Art Printmaking Course in an edition of 50

Bellany, John
Frost, Terry
Mara, Tim
Paolozzi, Eduardo
Rego, Paula
Shiomi, Nana

SIX ARTISTS, The 1994 Royal College of Art Portfolio of Prints, published by the Royal College of Art Printmaking Course (portfolio completed 1995) in an edition of 50

Caulfield, Patrick
Dunn, Alf
Irvin, Albert
Kunath, Rosalind
Pacheco, Ana Maria
Tilson, Joe

ACKROYD Norman B 1938
Spilling Cloud 1979

Etching, 34 × 54 plate; 50 × 65 sheet
65/90
Purchased from the artist September
1984
P4930

ACKROYD Norman B 1938
Rhum 1979

Etching, 34.3 × 54.4 plate; 50 × 65.5 sheet
Artist's proof
Purchased from the artist September
1984
P4931

ACKROYD Norman B 1938
Brightwater 1979

Etching, 39.5 × 53.5 plate; 50 × 65 sheet
10/90
Purchased from the artist September
1984
P4932

P4933

ACKROYD Norman B 1938
Woolstone Down 1980

Etching, 34.5 × 47.7 plate; 50.5 × 66 sheet
46/90
Purchased from the artist September
1984
P4933

ACKROYD Norman B 1938
Fonthill Revisited 1980

Etching, 41.7 × 42 plate; 57 × 50.5 sheet
51/90
Purchased from the artist September
1984
P4934

ACKROYD Norman B 1938
Swinbrook Meadows 1980

Etching, 34.3 × 54.4 plate; 50 × 65 sheet
81/90
Purchased from the artist September
1984
P4935

ACKROYD Norman B 1938
Westmere Evening 1980

Etching, 34.4 × 51.9 plate; 50 × 63.5 sheet
Artist's proof
Purchased from the artist September
1984
P4936

ACKROYD Norman B 1938
Westmere Night 1981

Etching, 34.2 × 51.5 plate; 50 × 64.5 sheet
59/90
Purchased from the artist September
1984
P4937

ACKROYD Norman B 1938
Beckfords Pond 1981

Etching, 42.3 × 42.3 plate;
60.5 × 56.5 sheet
142/150
Purchased from the artist September
1984
P4938

ACKROYD Norman B 1938
Wasdale Screes 1982

Etching, 34.3 × 48.9 plate; 50 × 65 sheet
2/90
Purchased from the artist September
1984
P4939

ACKROYD Norman B 1938
Wastwater 1982

Etching, 34.5 × 49 plate; 50 × 65.5 sheet
7/90
Purchased from the artist September
1984
P4940

ACKROYD Norman B 1938
Westmere Water 1982

Etching, 40 × 42.5 plate; 56 × 50.5 sheet
21/90
Purchased from the artist September
1984
P4941

ACKROYD Norman B 1938
Tree at Shoreham 1982

Etching, 41.4 × 41 plate; 56.5 × 50.5 sheet
Artist's proof
Purchased from the artist September
1984
P4942

ACKROYD Norman B 1938
Derwentwater 1982

Etching, 34.4 × 54.5 plate; 50 × 65 sheet
22/90
Purchased from the artist September
1984
P4943

ACKROYD Norman B 1938
**September Daybreak – Crockey
Hill** 1982

Etching, 41.4 × 41 plate; 60.5 × 56 sheet
63/90
Purchased from the artist September
1984
P4944

ACKROYD Norman B 1938
Sutton Mandeville – Walter's Path
1983

Etching, 59.9 × 88.9 plate;
71 × 100.3 sheet
1/40
Purchased from Thumb Gallery April
1984
P4863

ACKROYD Norman B 1938
Old Wardour Pool 1983

Etching, 59.9 × 88.9 plate;
71 × 100.3 sheet
9/40
Purchased from Thumb Gallery April
1984
P4864

ACKROYD Norman B 1938
The Lime Avenue – Avington 1984

Etching, 41 × 41.5 plate; 60.5 × 56 sheet
24/90
Purchased from the artist September
1984
P4945

ACKROYD Norman B 1938
Rackwick Valley III – Night 1984

Etching, 54 × 47 plate; 74 × 58.5 sheet
Artist's proof (final state)
Purchased from the artist September
1984
P4946

ACKROYD Norman B 1938
Loch and Birds 1984

Etching, 16.5 × 12.7 plate; 31 × 25 sheet
Artist's proof
Purchased from the artist September
1984
P4947

ACKROYD Norman B 1938
Hills and Rain 1984

Etching, 17.6 × 12.2 plate; 31 × 25 sheet
Artist's proof
Purchased from the artist September
1984
P4948

ACKROYD Norman B 1938
Wasdale Water 1984

Etching, 16 × 12.1 plate; 31 × 25 sheet
Artist's proof
Purchased from the artist September
1984
P4949

ACKROYD Norman B 1938
**It was seven o'clock when we got
into our boat . . .** 1987

From **Artists' Choice**, a portfolio of 48
prints by 48 artists, published 1987 by
the Royal College of Art Printmaking
Course
Etching, 11.5 × 16.3 plate; 30.5 × 30.5 sheet
4/48
Purchased from the Royal College of
Art Printmaking Course August 1987
P5552

ACKROYD Norman B 1938
Cormorant 1994

From **Nine London Birds**, a portfolio of
nine prints by nine artists, published
1994 by the Byam Shaw School of Art
Etching, 19.4 × 22.2 plate;
30.6 × 40.5 sheet
26/80
Purchased from the Byam Shaw School
of Art May 1994
P6274

AITCHISON Craigie B 1926
Wayney going to Heaven 1989

Screenprint, 21 × 15.5 image;
63 × 47 printed grey sheet
This print is not inscribed with an
edition number
Purchased from the National Art
Collections Fund September 1989
P5645

AITCHISON Craigie B 1926
Wayney going to Heaven 1989

Screenprint, 21 × 15.5 image;
63 × 47 printed grey sheet
58/75
Purchased from the National Art
Collections Fund December 1989
P5744   (colour plate 35)

AITCHISON Craigie B 1926
Wayney going to Heaven 1989

Screenprint, 21 × 15.5 image;
63 × 47 printed pink sheet
3/30
Purchased from the National Art
Collections Fund July 1991
P5948

AITCHISON Craigie B 1926
Magpie 1994

From **Nine London Birds**, a portfolio of
nine prints by nine artists, published
1994 by the Byam Shaw School of Art
Lithograph, 40.6 × 30.5 image and sheet
26/80
Purchased from the Byam Shaw School
of Art May 1994
P6275

AIVALIOTIS Sharon B 1951
Love is your last chance 1984

Mezzotint, 54 × 37 plate;
75 × 56.5 sheet
31/100
Presented by the artist December 1984
P4988

AIVALIOTIS Sharon B 1951
The Do-it-Yourself Suprematist Coffee-break 1985

Mezzotint and aquatint, 20.5 × 30 plate;
41 × 50.5 sheet
4/100
Purchased from Thumb Gallery
January 1986
P5341

P5342

AIVALIOTIS Sharon B 1951
Basics, Egg and Oil Emulsions 1985

Mezzotint, with hand colouring
29.5 × 38.5 plate; 52.5 × 65.5 sheet
9/100
Purchased from Thumb Gallery
January 1986
P5342

AIVALIOTIS Sharon B 1951
Pears 1985

Mezzotint and aquatint, with hand
colouring, 29.5 × 38.5 plate;
52.5 × 65.5 sheet
9/100
Purchased from Thumb Gallery
January 1986
P5343

ALLEN Richard B 1933
The Sign of the Cross

From Artists' Choice, a portfolio of 48
prints by 48 artists, published 1987 by
the Royal College of Art Printmaking
Course
Etching, 22.5 × 22.5 plate;
30.5 × 30.5 sheet
4/48
Purchased from the Royal College of
Art Printmaking Course August 1987
P5558

ALLEN Susie B 1949
Woodcutter cut my Shadow

From Artists' Choice, a portfolio of 48
prints by 48 artists, published 1987 by
the Royal College of Art Printmaking
Course
Lithograph, 17.8 × 17.2 image;
30.5 × 30.5 sheet
4/48
Purchased from the Royal College of
Art Printmaking Course August 1987
P5538

ATKINSON Conrad B 1940
The Wall Street Journal 1985

Lithograph, 56 × 40.6 image;
76.7 × 56.3 sheet
17/50
Purchased from Margaret Harrison,
representing Ronald Feldman Fine Arts
Inc., New York July 1987
P5506

ATKINSON Conrad B 1940
Two screenprints, 1988, from an
untitled set of four screenprints
Published 1988 by the artist and
Peacock Printmakers, Aberdeen in
an edition of 30
Purchased from Margaret Harrison,
representing Ronald Feldman Fine Arts
Inc., New York July 1988
P5610, P5611

Thanx Andy

113.3 × 76.5 image and sheet
21/30
P5610

Thanx Picasso

112.3 × 76.8 image and sheet
22/30
P5611

ATKINSON Conrad B 1940
An untitled set of three etchings with
acrylic paint 1989
Each plate 23.7 × 21.5; sheet 40 × 37
Published by Solo Press Inc. and State
Editions, New York 1989
Edition of 40
Purchased from Margaret Harrison,
representing Ronald Feldman Fine Arts
Inc., New York February 1991
P5858, P5859, P5860

Aesthetics

Artist's proof 2
P5858

Passion/Post Modern

Artist's proof 16
P5859

Fantasy/Desire

Artist's proof 2
P5860

AYRES Gillian B 1930
Crystal Fields 1987

From Artists' Choice, a portfolio of 48
prints by 48 artists, published 1987 by
the Royal College of Art Printmaking
Course
Lithograph, 30.5 × 30.5 image and sheet
4/48
Purchased from the Royal College of
Art Printmaking Course August 1987
P5541

BAWDEN Edward 1903-1989
Following the publication of Edward
Bawden's large linocut **Jonah's Whale**
in 1987, Merivale Editions embarked on
a major project to edition the best of the
linocuts collected over the years in the
artist's studio. These were printed by
hand under Bawden's direction on his
own Albion press by his grandson,
Philip. The printing was completed and
the edition numbered, titled and signed
shortly before Bawden's death in 1989.

BAWDEN Edward 1903–1989
A Nautical Design undated

Linocut, 26.6 × 14 image; 45.7 × 38 sheet
8/25
Purchased from Merivale Editions
November 1989
P5721

BAWDEN Edward 1903–1989
A Voyage c.1950

Linocut, 8.3 × 19 image; 38 × 45.7 sheet
13/25
Purchased from Merivale Editions
November 1989
P5713

BAWDEN Edward 1903–1989
A Jaunting-car c.1950

Linocut, 16.5 × 23.5 image;
38 × 45.7 sheet
7/25
Purchased from Merivale Editions
November 1989
P5715

BAWDEN Edward 1903–1989
The Monument 1952

Linocut, 31.1 × 10.1 image;
45.7 × 38 sheet
7/10
Purchased from Merivale Editions
November 1989
P5714

BAWDEN Edward 1903–1989
St. Paul's 1952

Linocut, 19.7 × 15.2 image;
45.7 × 38 sheet
13/25
Purchased from Merivale Editions
November 1989
P5716

BAWDEN Edward 1903–1989
Aries 1954

Linocut, 10.2 × 8.9 image; 45.7 × 38 sheet
6/10
Purchased from Merivale Editions
November 1989
P5712

P5722

BAWDEN Edward 1903–1989
The Flight from the Enchanter
1956

Linocut, 10.8 × 15.3 image;
38 × 45.7 sheet
8/15
Purchased from Merivale Editions
November 1989
P5722

BAWDEN Edward 1903–1989
Mother & Chicks c.1959

Linocut, 13.3 × 17.8 image;
38 × 45.7 sheet
13/25
Purchased from Merivale Editions
November 1989
P5718

BAWDEN Edward 1903–1989
Queen Elizabeth 1964

Linocut, 21 × 10.8 image; 45.7 × 38 sheet
7/15
Purchased from Merivale Editions
November 1989
P5717

BAWDEN Edward 1903–1989
The Rocket 1964

Linocut, 8.9 × 15.9 image; 38 × 45.7 sheet
7/25
Purchased from Merivale Editions
November 1989
P5719

BAWDEN Edward 1903–1989
Queen Victoria c.1965

Linocut, 22.9 × 20.3 image;
45.7 × 38 sheet
7/25
Purchased from Merivale Editions
November 1989
P5720

BAWDEN Edward 1903–1989
Aesop's Fables: The Daw in Borrowed Feathers 1970

Linocut, 40.4 × 56.7 image
Artist's proof 5/50
Purchased from The Fine Art Society
March 1994
P6212

BAWDEN Edward 1903–1989
**Aesop's Fables: The Peacock &
Magpie** 1970

Linocut, 40.8 × 56 image
Artist's proof 46/50
Purchased from The Fine Art Society
March 1994

P6213

BAWDEN Edward 1903–1989
**Aesop's Fables: The Gnat & the
Lion** 1970

Linocut, 40.6 × 56 image
Artist's proof 4/60
Purchased from The Fine Art Society
March 1994

P6214

BAWDEN Edward 1903–1989
**Tyger! Tyger! burning bright in
the forests of the night . . .** 1974

Linocut, 20.2 × 63 image
This print is not inscribed with an
edition number
Purchased from The Fine Art Society
March 1994

P6211

The title of this print was subsequently
shortened to **Tyger! Tyger!**

BAWDEN Edward 1903–1989
Jonah's Whale 1987

Linocut, 25.4 × 63.5 image;
67.3 × 96.5 sheet
78/100
Purchased from Merivale Editions
November 1989

P5723

BAWDEN Edward 1903–1989
Lion and Zebras 1989

Linocut, 50.8 × 76.5 sheet
14/75
Purchased from the National Art
Collections Fund September 1989

P5643

BAWDEN Edward 1903–1989
Indian Elephant 1989

Linocut, 30.1 × 29.5 image;
57.3 × 50.1 sheet
9/25
Purchased from the National Art
Collections Fund November 1989

P5709

BAWDEN Edward 1903–1989
Our Family I 1989

Linocut, 63.1 × 90.8 image and sheet
18/100
Purchased from the National Art
Collections Fund November 1989

P5710

BAWDEN Edward 1903–1989
Indian Elephant 1989

Linocut, 30.1 × 29.5 image; 57.3 × 50.1 sheet
21/25
Purchased from the National Art
Collections Fund July 1991

P5949

BAWDEN Edward 1903–1989
Indian Elephant 1989

Linocut, 30.1 × 29.5 image; 57.3 × 50.1 sheet
25/25
Presented by the National Art
Collections Fund July 1991

P5950

BAXTER Glen B 1944
Glen Baxter Presents 1984

A set of five lithographs
Standard sheet size:
portrait 77.7 × 57.2;
landscape 57.2 × 77.7
Published by Nigel Greenwood 1984
Numbered 106 of an edition of 200
Purchased from Nigel Greenwood
Gallery June 1986

P5392–P5396

Saturday Morning Shopping

77.7 × 57.2 image and sheet
P5392

Brenda

77.7 × 57.2 image and sheet
P5393

Sunset

57.2 × 77.7 image and sheet
P5394

The Cricket Match

77.7 × 57.2 image and sheet
P5395

The 4th Time

57.2 × 77.7 image and sheet
P5396

BELLANY John B 1942
Three etchings, 1986, from **The Scottish
Bestiary**, 20 prints in various media,
various sizes, by seven Scottish artists
illustrating the writings in poetry and
prose of George Mackay Brown
Published 1986 by Charles Booth-
Clibborn under his imprint The
Paragon Press in a book edition of 60
and a portfolio edition of 50
Purchased from The Paragon Press
December 1986

P5461, P5466, P5468

Eagle

56 × 76 sheet (image and text)
Book edition: 26/60
P5461

Grouse/Capercaillie

56 × 76 sheet (image and text)
Book edition: 26/60
P5466

Wildcat

56 × 76 sheet (image and text)
Book edition: 26/60
P5468

BELLANY John B 1942
Jeune Fille, Le Tréport 1986

Etching, 32.5 × 24.5 plate;
56.5 × 37.7 sheet
4/25
Purchased from Edinburgh
Printmakers December 1989

P5731

BELLANY John B 1942
Achates 1986

Etching, 39 × 33 plate; 65 × 50.5 sheet
4/50
Purchased from Edinburgh
Printmakers December 1989

P5732

BELLANY John B 1942
Two works from **Images Inspired by
Ernest Hemingway's 'The Old Man and
the Sea'**, a portfolio of 14 prints (four
screenprints and ten etchings), made by
the artist between October 1986 and
May 1987
Published 1987 by Charles Booth-
Clibborn under his imprint The
Paragon Press in an edition of 60
portfolios and 15 additional sets
numbered I to XV
Purchased from The Paragon Press
October 1989

P5661, P5662

Untitled

Etching, 32.2 × 47.8 plate;
56.8 × 75.7 sheet
XV/XV
P5661

Untitled

Screenprint, 56.8 × 75.7 image and sheet
XV/XV
P5662

BELLANY John B 1942
Serendipity

From **Artists' Choice**, a portfolio of 48
prints by 48 artists, published 1987 by
the Royal College of Art Printmaking
Course
Etching, 22.3 × 22.5 plate;
30.5 × 30.5 sheet
4/48
Purchased from the Royal College of
Art Printmaking Course August 1987

P5546

BELLANY John B 1942
**Self Portrait (Addenbrooke's
Hospital 1988)** 1989

Etching, 121 × 110 plate; 134 × 117.5 sheet
11/20
Purchased from Peacock Printmakers,
Aberdeen August 1989

P5642

P6188

BELLANY John B 1942
Celtic Voyage 1992

From **Six Artists, The 1992 Royal
College of Art Portfolio of Prints**,
published by the Royal College of Art
Printmaking Course
Lithograph, 76 × 56.5 image and sheet
26/50
Purchased from the Royal College of
Art Printmaking Course March 1993

P6188

BELLANY John B 1942
Gull 1994

From **Nine London Birds**, a portfolio of
nine prints by nine artists, published
1994 by the Byam Shaw School of Art
Etching, 24.7 × 19.8 plate; 41 × 30.3 sheet
26/80
Purchased from the Byam Shaw School
of Art May 1994

P6276

BERG Adrian B 1929
W B Yeats' "Lapis Lazuli"

From **Artists' Choice**, a portfolio of 48
prints by 48 artists, published 1987 by
the Royal College of Art Printmaking
Course
Screenprint, 23 × 19.5 image;
30.5 × 30.5 sheet
4/48
Purchased from the Royal College of
Art Printmaking Course August 1987

P5515

BICÂT André B 1909
Tuscan Bunch

From **Artists' Choice**, a portfolio of 48
prints by 48 artists, published 1987 by
the Royal College of Art Printmaking
Course
Lithograph, 30.5 × 30.5 image and sheet
4/48
Purchased from the Royal College of
Art Printmaking Course August 1987

P5524

BLACKADDER Elizabeth B 1931
Still Life with Iris 1989

Etching, aquatint and gold leaf
42.9 × 52.5 plate; 53 × 70 sheet
11/75
Purchased from the National Art
Collections Fund September 1989

P5644

BLAKE Peter B 1932
Study for a Poster for Frankenstein
Performed by the GRÆÆ Theatre Co.

From **Artists' Choice**, a portfolio of 48 prints by 48 artists, published 1987 by the Royal College of Art Printmaking Course
Lithograph, 20 × 20 image; 30.5 × 30.5 sheet
4/48
Purchased from the Royal College of Art Printmaking Course August 1987
P5519

BLAKE Peter B 1932
Alphabet 1991

A series of 26 screenprints
Each sheet 103 × 77.5; image sizes vary
Published by Waddington Graphics 1991
Numbered 32 of an edition of 95
Purchased from Waddington Galleries May 1991
P5977 – P6002

A for Alphabet

72.2 × 50.5 image
P5977

B for Boxer

73.2 × 52 image
P5978

C for Clowning

72.3 × 53 image
P5979

D for Dwarfs and Midgets

72 × 50.7 image
P5980

E for Everly Brothers

72.4 × 50.8 image
P5981

F for Football

73.1 × 50.8 image
P5982

G for Girl

72.4 × 50.8 image
P5983

H for Heart

72.4 × 50.8 image
P5984

I for Idols

72.1 × 50.6 image
P5985

J for James Dean

72.4 × 50.8 image
P5986

K for King (Elvis Presley)

72 × 50.5 image
P5987

L for Love

72.4 × 50.8 image
P5988

M for Marilyn Monroe

72.5 × 50.8 image
P5989

N for Nude

72.4 × 50.8 image
P5990

O for Ornithology

72.4 × 50.8 image
P5991

P for Pachyderm

72 × 50.6 image
P5992

Q for Quarters

72.4 × 50.8 image
P5993

R for Rainbow

72.4 × 50.3 image
P5994

S for Sumo

72.4 × 50.8 image
P5995

T for The Beatles

72.4 × 50.8 image
P5996

U for Unusual People

72 × 50.6 image
P5997

V for Valentine

72.4 × 50.8 image
P5998

W for Wrestler
(from a photograph by Terence Donovan)
72.4 × 50.8 image
P5999

X for Xylophonist

72.7 × 50.6 image
P6000

Y for Yacht

72.4 × 50.8 image
P6001

Z for Zebra

72.4 × 50.8 image
P6002

BLAKE Quentin B 1932
In the Afternoon

From **Artists' Choice**, a portfolio of 48 prints by 48 artists, published 1987 by the Royal College of Art Printmaking Course
Lithograph, 30.5 × 30.5 image and sheet
4/48
Purchased from the Royal College of Art Printmaking Course August 1987
P5535

BOND Henry B 1966
Untitled 1994

From "Other Men's Flowers", text works by 15 London based artists, curated by Joshua Compston, and published 1994 by Charles Booth-Clibborn under his imprint The Paragon Press
Letterpress, 61 × 47 sheet
18/100
Purchased from The Paragon Press November 1994
P6293

BRISLEY Stuart B 1933
Untitled 1994

From "Other Men's Flowers", text works by 15 London based artists, curated by Joshua Compston, and published 1994 by Charles Booth-Clibborn under his imprint The Paragon Press
Letterpress, 61 × 47 sheet
18/100
Purchased from The Paragon Press November 1994
P6294

BROWN Don B 1962
Untitled 1994

From "Other Men's Flowers", text works by 15 London based artists, curated by Joshua Compston, and published 1994 by Charles Booth-Clibborn under his imprint The Paragon Press
Letterpress, 61 × 47 sheet
18/100
Purchased from The Paragon Press November 1994
P6295

BUCKLEY Stephen B 1944
Mercer 1986

From **Artists' Choice**, a portfolio of 48 prints by 48 artists, published 1987 by the Royal College of Art Printmaking Course
Etching, 19 × 12.5 plate; 30.5 × 30.5 sheet
4/48
Purchased from the Royal College of Art Printmaking Course August 1987
P5530

BURTON Clive B 1947
"Ysabel's Table Dance" (by Charlie Mingus) 1987

From **Artists' Choice**, a portfolio of 48 prints by 48 artists, published 1987 by the Royal College of Art Printmaking Course
Etching, 12.7 × 9.5 left plate; 12.8 × 8.2 right plate; 30.5 × 30.5 sheet
4/48
Purchased from the Royal College of Art Printmaking Course August 1987
P5556

CAMP Jeffery B 1923
Pigeons 1994

From **Nine London Birds**, a portfolio of nine prints by nine artists, published 1994 by the Byam Shaw School of Art
Lithograph, 30.6 × 40.8 image and sheet
26/80
Purchased from the Byam Shaw School of Art May 1994
P6277

P5627

CAMPBELL Steven B 1953
Gesturing Hiker 1983

Woodcut, 150.5 × 120 image; 166.5 × 132 sheet
Artist's proof 4/5
Purchased from Barbara Toll Fine Arts, New York February 1989
P5627

CAMPBELL Steven B 1953
The Hiker said, "Death, you shall not take the Child" 1983

Woodcut, printed on two sheets of Japanese paper, 244 × 244 overall image
11/15
Purchased at Sotheby's, New York, through The Paragon Press February 1990
P5768

CAMPBELL Steven B 1953
Two woodcuts, 1986, from **The Scottish Bestiary**, 20 prints in various media, various sizes, by seven Scottish artists illustrating the writings in poetry and prose of George Mackay Brown
Published 1986 by Charles Booth-Clibborn under his imprint The Paragon Press in a book edition of 60 and a portfolio edition of 50
Purchased from The Paragon Press December 1986
P5451, P5469

Frontispiece

56 × 76 sheet (image and text)
Book edition: 26/60
P5451

Lobster

56 × 76 sheet (image and text)
Book edition: 26/60
P5469

Caro Anthony B 1924
Nude

From **Artists' Choice**, a portfolio of 48 prints by 48 artists, published 1987 by the Royal College of Art Printmaking Course
Lithograph, 30.5 × 30.5 image and sheet
4/48
Purchased from the Royal College of Art Printmaking Course August 1987
P5525

Castle Christopher B 1946
Giant's Ring – Giantess' Apronful 1979

Etching and screenprint
54.4 × 41.3 plate; 68.8 × 52.5 sheet
11/50
Purchased from Thumb Gallery April 1984
P4868

Castle Christopher B 1946
Funnel Beaker at Sarnowo 1981

Etching and screenprint
54 × 43 plate; 71.5 × 50.5 sheet
Artist's proof 1/5
Purchased from Thumb Gallery April 1984
P4867

Castle Christopher B 1946
Cromlech at Xarez, Portugal 1982

Etching and screenprint
43.8 × 68.4 plate; 56 × 75.7 sheet
Artist's proof 8/25
Purchased from Thumb Gallery April 1984
P4866

Castle Christopher B 1946
A Message from Scorhill, Dartmoor 1983

Etching and screenprint
38 × 64.8 overall plate; 50.3 × 72 sheet
Artist's proof
Purchased from Thumb Gallery April 1984
P4865

Caulfield Patrick B 1936
The Poems of Jules Laforgue 1973

The English edition of a book of 12 poems together with a portfolio of 22 screenprints
Each image 40.5 × 35.5; sheet 61 × 56
Published by Petersburg Press in collaboration with Waddington Galleries 1973
Numbered 35 of an edition of 100
Purchased from Waddington Galleries March 1985
P5031 – P5052

Ah! this Life is so everyday

P5031 (colour plate 36)

Watch me eat, without appetite, à la carte

P5032

She fled along the avenue

P5033

Her handkerchief swept me along the Rhine

P5034

Crying to the walls: My God! My God! Will she relent?

P5035

You'll be sick if you spend all your time indoors

P5036

I'll take my life monotonous

P5037

All these confessions . . .

P5038

Making circles on park lagoons

P5039

Oh! if one of Them, some fine evening, would try

P5040

Thus she would come, escaped, half-dead to my door

P5041

And, with my eyes bolting toward the Unconscious

P5042

We wanted to bleed the Silence

P5043

Along a twilighted sky

P5044

Oh Helen, I roam my room

P5045

I've only the friendship of hotel rooms

P5046

She'll have forgotten her scarf

P5047

And I am alone in my house

P5048

All the benches are wet, the woods are so rusty

P5049

Ah! storm clouds rushed from the Channel coasts

P5050

Curtains drawn back from balconies of shores

P5051

My life inspires so many desires!

P5052

Caulfield Patrick B 1936
Pool 1975

Tapestry/wall hanging, hand knotted in India, 248.9 × 198.2
Artist's proof
Purchased from Waddington Galleries January 1991
P5847

Caulfield Patrick B 1936
Pool 1975

Tapestry/wall hanging, hand knotted in India, 248.9 × 198.2
14/25
Purchased from Waddington Galleries July 1991
P5965

Caulfield Patrick B 1936
Fruit and Bowl 1979

Screenprint, 83.8 × 59.7 image and sheet
11/100
Purchased from Waddington Galleries March 1985
P5026

Caulfield Patrick B 1936
Plant Pot 1979

Screenprint, 83.8 × 59.7 image and sheet
89/100
Purchased from Waddington Galleries March 1985
P5027

Caulfield Patrick B 1936
Cream Glazed Pot 1979

Screenprint, 83.8 × 59.7 image and sheet
Artist's proof 10/15
Purchased from Waddington Galleries March 1985
P5028

Caulfield Patrick B 1936
Ridged Jar 1980

Screenprint, 83.8 × 59.7 image and sheet
40/40
Purchased from Waddington Galleries March 1985
P5029

Caulfield Patrick B 1936
Fern Pot 1980

Screenprint, 83.8 × 59.7 image and sheet
48/65
Purchased from Waddington Galleries March 1985
P5030

Caulfield Patrick B 1936
White Ware Prints 1990

A series of eight screenprints
Each 107.3 × 81.3 image and sheet
Published by Waddington Graphics 1990
Numbered 23 of an edition of 45
Purchased from Waddington Galleries October 1990
P5819 – P5826

P5819

Large White Jug

P5819

Lamp and Kuan Ware

P5820

Lung Ch'uan Ware and Window

P5821

Lung Ch'uan Ware and Black Lamp

P5822

Lamp and Lung Ch'uan Ware

P5823

Arita Flask

P5824

Arita Flask – black

P5825

Sue Ware Jar

P5826

Caulfield Patrick B 1936
Duck 1994

From **Nine London Birds**, a portfolio of nine prints by nine artists, published 1994 by the Byam Shaw School of Art
Screenprint, 40.3 × 30.5 image and sheet
26/80
Purchased from the Byam Shaw School of Art May 1994
P6278

Caulfield Patrick B 1936
Wall Lamp 1994

From **Six Artists, The 1994 Royal College of Art Portfolio of Prints**, published by the Royal College of Art Printmaking Course (portfolio completed 1995)
Screenprint, 76.1 × 56 image and sheet
26/50
Purchased from the Royal College of Art Printmaking Course June 1994
P6308

CHADWICK Helen B 1953
Untitled 1994

From "Other Men's Flowers", text
works by 15 London based artists,
curated by Joshua Compston, and
published 1994 by Charles Booth-
Clibborn under his imprint The
Paragon Press
Letterpress, 47 × 61 sheet
18/100
Purchased from The Paragon Press
November 1994
P6296

CHAPLIN Bob B 1947
**Timelapse Panorama – Priddy
Nine Barrows, Mendips** 1977

Screenprint with etching
35 × 71.2 image; 50.5 × 77 sheet
Artist's proof
Purchased from the artist September
1984
P4920

CHAPLIN Bob B 1947
**Timelapse Panorama – Stanton
Drew, Mendips** 1977

Screenprint with etching
35 × 71.2 image; 50.5 × 77 sheet
Artist's proof
Purchased from the artist September
1984
P4921

CHAPLIN Bob B 1947
Seven Sisters a.m./p.m. 1978

Screenprint with etching
41.3 × 69.5 image; 56.3 × 76 sheet
47/50
Purchased from the artist September
1984
P4918

CHAPLIN Bob B 1947
**Timelapse Panorama – Hadrian's
Wall** 1978

Screenprint with etching
33.7 × 69.5 image; 50.5 × 77 sheet
Artist's proof
Purchased from the artist September
1984
P4922

CHAPLIN Bob B 1947
Seven Sisters – One Hour's Walk
1979

Screenprint with etching
42 × 70 image; 56 × 76 sheet
37/45
Purchased from the artist September
1984
P4917

CHAPLIN Bob B 1947
**High Tide/Low Tide – Beachy
Head** 1979

Screenprint, 42.3 × 62.2 image;
50.8 × 68.5 sheet
24/45
Purchased from the artist September
1984
P4919

CHAPLIN Bob B 1947
Mountain Bay : Hoy Orkney 1981

Screenprint with letterpress
49 × 69 image; 56.5 × 76.5 sheet
Artist's proof
Purchased from the artist September
1984
P4924

CHAPLIN Bob B 1947
Sound Headland : Eday Orkney
1982

Screenprint with letterpress
49 × 69 image; 56.5 × 76.5 sheet
Artist's proof
Purchased from the artist September
1984
P4923

CHAPLIN Bob B 1947
**Vineyard – Flintfield – Breaky
Bottom** 1982

Screenprint with etching
67 × 50 image; 75.5 × 56 sheet
Artist's proof
Purchased from the artist September
1984
P4925

CHAPLIN Bob B 1947
**Lake District I – Dow Crag Goat
Water** 1983

Etching, 25.5 × 34.5 plate;
50.5 × 65.5 sheet
Artist's proof
Purchased from Thumb Gallery April
1984
P4869

CHAPLIN Bob B 1947
**Lake District II – Brown Pike
Blind Tarn** 1983

Etching, 26 × 34.5 plate; 50 × 65.5 sheet
Artist's proof
Purchased from Thumb Gallery April
1984
P4870

CHAPLIN Bob B 1947
**From Nethermost Pike to
Helvellyn** 1983

Etching with text, 13.7 × 45.7 plate;
50.3 × 65.5 sheet
Artist's proof
Purchased from Thumb Gallery April
1984
P4871

CHAPLIN Bob B 1947
**Dollywagon Pike Looking Over to
Great Rigg Man** 1983

Etching with text, 13.7 × 45.7 plate;
50.3 × 65.5 sheet
Artist's proof
Purchased from Thumb Gallery April
1984
P4872

CHAPLIN Bob B 1947
**Flintfield – Vineyard – Breaky
Bottom** 1983

Screenprint with etching
67 × 50 image; 76 × 56 sheet
Artist's proof
Purchased from the artist September
1984
P4926

CHAPLIN Bob B 1947
Two screenprints, 1986, from **Working
Material I – IV**, a suite of four
screenprints
Published 1986 by The Retigraphic
Society in an edition of 60
Purchased from The Retigraphic
Society, Ightham, Kent November 1986
P5429, P5430

**Working Material I – Mother
Zebra, Lofoten, North Norway**

109 × 74 image and sheet
7/60
P5429

**Working Material IV – Lysefjord,
Southern Norway**

109 × 74 image and sheet
7/60
P5430

P6279

CLOUGH Prunella B 1919
Starlings 1994

From **Nine London Birds**, a portfolio of
nine prints by nine artists, published
1994 by the Byam Shaw School of Art
Etching, 17.6 × 22.6 plate; 30.2 × 41.5 sheet
26/80
Purchased from the Byam Shaw School
of Art May 1994
P6279

COLLINS Cecil 1908–1989
Fool Carrying a Child 1987

From Artists' Choice, a portfolio of 48
prints by 48 artists, published 1987 by
the Royal College of Art Printmaking
Course
Etching, 20.1 × 15 plate; 30.5 × 30.5 sheet
4/48
Purchased from the Royal College of
Art Printmaking Course August 1987
P5555

COLLISHAW Mat B 1966
Untitled 1994

From "Other Men's Flowers", text
works by 15 London based artists,
curated by Joshua Compston, and
published 1994 by Charles Booth-
Clibborn under his imprint The
Paragon Press
Blind embossed letterpress, 61 × 47 sheet
18/100
Purchased from The Paragon Press
November 1994
P6297

COOPER Eileen B 1953
The Healer 1989

Etching, 37 × 50 plate; 57.7 × 76.2 sheet
2/35
Purchased from Curwen Gallery
February 1990
P5764

COOPER Eileen B 1953
Learning to Fly 1989

Etching, 31.3 × 23.7 plate; 65.3 × 54 sheet
2/35
Purchased from Curwen Gallery
February 1990
P5765

CRAGG Tony B 1949
Marbleized Set 1988

A series of five aquatints
Each plate 30.5 × 34.9; sheet 58.4 × 60.9
Published by Crown Point Press, San
Francisco 1988
Numbered 3 of an edition of 15
Purchased from Crown Point Press, San
Francisco June 1989
P5635 – P5639

Horns 1
P5635

Horns 2
P5636

Spores
P5637

Vessels
P5638

Untitled
P5639

CRAIG-MARTIN Michael B 1941
Order of Appearance 1990

A series of four screenprints
Each 118 × 83.2 image and sheet
Published by Waddington Graphics
1990
Numbered 42 of an edition of 50
Purchased from Waddington Galleries
January 1991
P5848–P5851

Order of Appearance: Book

P5848

Order of Appearance: Cassette

P5849

P5850

Order of Appearance: Canvas

P5850

Order of Appearance: Drawer

P5851

CRAWFORD Alistair B 1945
Two etchings, 1976, from the series
Welsh Landscape Variations I–VII
Published by the artist 1976–84 in an
edition of 15, with the exception of
**Welsh Landscape Variations VII
(Moon & Harbour Wall)** which is
published in an edition of 35
Purchased from Curwen Gallery
November 1984
P4982, P4983

Welsh Landscape Variations I

12.3 × 16.5 plate (irregular);
23.7 × 25 sheet
10/15
P4982

Welsh Landscape Variations II

12.3 × 16.1 plate (irregular);
23.7 × 25 sheet
10/15
P4983

CRAWFORD Alistair B 1945
Hills, Sea and Clouds 1977

Etching and aquatint, 19.3 × 29.2 plate;
64.7 × 49 sheet
16/23
Purchased from Curwen Gallery
September 1984
P4952

CRAWFORD Alistair B 1945
The Four Seasons 1978

A set of four lithographs with crayon
and pencil
Each image 18.5 × 27.5; sheet 20.5 × 28.5
Published by the artist 1978
Numbered 7 of an edition of 75
Purchased from Curwen Gallery
November 1984
P4984 – P4987

Four Seasons – Spring

P4984

Four Seasons – Summer

P4985

Four Seasons – Autumn

P4986

Four Seasons – Winter

P4987

CRAWFORD Alistair B 1945
Ploughed Fields 1979

Etching and aquatint
34.3 × 26.8 plate (irregular);
64.7 × 49 sheet
18/30
Purchased from Curwen Gallery
September 1984
P4951

CRAWFORD Alistair B 1945
Harbour Wall 1980

Etching and aquatint
33 × 26.8 plate (irregular);
64.7 × 49 sheet
8/18
Purchased from Curwen Gallery
September 1984
P4950

CRAWFORD Alistair B 1945
Rain 1980

Etching and aquatint, 33.5 × 26.8 plate;
64.7 × 49 sheet
9/30
Purchased from Curwen Gallery
September 1984
P4953

CRAWFORD Alistair B 1945
Dyfed Landscapes 1981

A portfolio of four etchings and
aquatints with screenprinted text, and
one screenprinted text sheet, illustrating
poems by Moelwyn Merchant
Each plate 25 × 25.1; sheet 53 × 43.5
Published by the artist 1981
Numbered 6 of an edition of 35
Purchased from Curwen Gallery
September 1984
P4954 – P4958

Ann Williams

P4954

Revealing a Skull

P4955

**"There are certain things you
cannot say about a stone . . ."**

P4956

Miracles at Llanddewibrefi

P4957

Envoi

Screenprinted text sheet, 53 × 43.5
P4958

CRAWFORD Alistair B 1945
View from a Window 1984

A set of five lithographs with hand
colouring
Each sheet 26 × 34; image sizes vary
Published by the artist 1984
Numbered 47 of an edition of 150, with
the exception of **East Coast of Scotland**
which is numbered 47 of an edition of
200
Presented by the artist January 1985
P4989 – P4993

East Coast of Scotland

20.5 × 22 image
P4989

San Gimignano, Tuscany, Italy

19.4 × 20.9 image
P4990

Mykonos, Greece

20 × 26.6 image
P4991

**La Roque – Gegeac, Dordogne,
France**

19.4 × 22.3 image
P4992

Tucson, Arizona, U S A

19.4 × 22 image
P4993

CROWLEY Graham B 1950
Untitled 1986

Linocut, 60 × 52.5 image; 66 × 64 sheet
Artist's proof
Purchased from Edward Totah Gallery
December 1987
P5578

CULBERT Bill B 1935
Decant 1987 1987

From **Artists' Choice**, a portfolio of 48
prints by 48 artists, published 1987 by
the Royal College of Art Printmaking
Course
Photoprint, 16 × 11.5 image;
30.5 × 30.5 sheet
4/48
Purchased from the Royal College of
Art Printmaking Course August 1987
P5522

P5628

CURRIE Ken B 1960
Union Organiser 1987

Lithograph, 68 × 51 image; 76 × 56 sheet
20/20
Purchased from Edinburgh
Printmakers March 1989
P5628

CURRIE Ken B 1960
The Self-Taught Man 1987

Lithograph, 68 × 51 image; 76 × 56 sheet
36/50
Purchased from Edinburgh
Printmakers December 1989
P5742

CURRIE Ken B 1960
Ten linocuts (including frontispiece),
1989, from **Story from Glasgow**, a
portfolio of 97 black and white linocuts
Each image 29 × 25; sheet 43 × 32.2
Frontispiece 40.5 × 30.3
Published 1989 by Charles Booth-
Clibborn under his imprint The
Paragon Press, in a book edition of 50
and a portfolio edition of 45
Numbered 18 of the portfolio edition of
45
Purchased from The Paragon Press
October 1989
P5651 – P5660

DAVIE Alan B 1920
Magic Reader 1988

A portfolio of 18 lithographs
Each sheet 42.6 × 34.8; image sizes vary
Published by Charles Booth-Clibborn
under his imprint The Paragon Press
1988
Numbered 30 of an edition of 45
Purchased from The Paragon Press
December 1991
P6013 – P6030

Untitled

20.2 × 18.7 image
P6013

Untitled

19 × 28.5 image
P6014

Untitled

21 × 25 image
P6015

Untitled

34 × 28 image
P6016

P6017

Untitled

19 × 28.5 image
P6017

Untitled

27.5 × 29.5
P6018

Untitled

28.5 × 30.5 image
P6019

Untitled

28.5 × 24.5 image
P6020

Untitled

20.5 × 25.5 image
P6021

Untitled

29.8 × 27.5 image
P6022

Untitled

26.3 × 25 image
P6023

Untitled

15 × 17.5 image
P6024

Untitled

26.8 × 30 image
P6025

Untitled

25.4 × 28 image
P6026

Untitled

24 × 28.5 image
P6027

Untitled

30 × 28 image
P6028

Untitled

30 × 24.8 image
P6029

Untitled

37 × 30 image
P6030

DAVIES Anthony B 1947

Northern Ireland 1987

From **Artists' Choice**, a portfolio of 48 prints by 48 artists, published 1987 by the Royal College of Art Printmaking Course

Lithograph, 30.5 × 30.5 image and sheet
4/48

Purchased from the Royal College of Art Printmaking Course August 1987
P5526

DAVIES Anthony B 1947

The Great Divide 1 1987

Lithograph, 62 × 81.5 image;
75 × 111 sheet
38/60

Purchased from Thumb Gallery December 1989
P5745

DEACON Richard B 1949

Muzot 1987

A portfolio of four prints
Various media, various sizes
Published by Margarete Roeder Editions, New York 1987
Numbered 8 of an edition of 25
Purchased from Lisson Gallery March 1988
P5582 – P5585

Muzot 1

Aquatint and lithographic crayon
64.4 × 64.1 image and sheet
P5582

Muzot 2

Etching, 64.4 × 64.4 image and sheet
P5583

P5584

Muzot 3

Etching, with embossing on toile cirée (plastic canvas laminate with wood-grain), 40 × 58 plate; 64 × 64 toile cirée
P5584

Muzot 4

Aquatint, with embossing on toile cirée (plastic canvas laminate with wood-grain), 57 × 57 plate; 64 × 64 toile cirée
P5585

DENIS Dominic B 1963

Untitled 1992

From **London**, a portfolio of 11 prints made by 11 artists working in London, published 1992 by Charles Booth-Clibborn under his imprint The Paragon Press

Screenprint, 59.6 × 68.5 image;
76 × 82.5 sheet
38/65

Purchased from Karsten Schubert, London June 1992
P6066

DENNY Robyn B 1930

Hand Job 1987

From **Artists' Choice**, a portfolio of 48 prints by 48 artists, published 1987 by the Royal College of Art Printmaking Course

Hand finished lithograph
30.5 × 30.5 image and sheet
4/48

Purchased from the Royal College of Art Printmaking Course August 1987
P5550

DORON Itai B 1967

Untitled 1994

From **"Other Men's Flowers"**, text works by 15 London based artists, curated by Joshua Compston, and published 1994 by Charles Booth-Clibborn under his imprint The Paragon Press

Letterpress, 61 × 47 sheet
18/100

Purchased from The Paragon Press November 1994
P6298

DUNN Alf B 1937

"In Vacant or in Pensive Mood"
1986

From **Artists' Choice**, a portfolio of 48 prints by 48 artists, published 1987 by the Royal College of Art Printmaking Course

Screenprint and lithograph
30.5 × 30.5 image and sheet
4/48

Purchased from the Royal College of Art Printmaking Course August 1987
P5545

DUNN Alf B 1937

Touching Reality 1994

From **Six Artists, The 1994 Royal College of Art Portfolio of Prints**, published by the Royal College of Art Printmaking Course (portfolio completed 1995)

Lithograph with screenprinting
55.3 × 76.2 image and sheet
26/50

Purchased from the Royal College of Art Printmaking Course June 1994
P6309

EDWARDS Jeffery B 1945

Eve 1987

From **Artists' Choice**, a portfolio of 48 prints by 48 artists, published 1987 by the Royal College of Art Printmaking Course

Screenprint, 30.5 × 30.5 image and sheet
4/48

Purchased from the Royal College of Art Printmaking Course August 1987
P5516

EMIN Tracey B 1963

Untitled 1994

From **"Other Men's Flowers"**, text works by 15 London based artists, curated by Joshua Compston, and published 1994 by Charles Booth-Clibborn under his imprint The Paragon Press

Letterpress, 61 × 47 sheet
18/100

Purchased from The Paragon Press November 1994
P6299

P6067

FAIRHURST Angus B 1966

When I woke up in the morning, the feeling was still there. 1992

From **London**, a portfolio of 11 prints made by 11 artists working in London, published 1992 by Charles Booth-Clibborn under his imprint The Paragon Press

Screenprint with varnish
86.5 × 65.8 image and sheet
38/65

Purchased from Karsten Schubert, London June 1992
P6067

FAIRHURST Angus B 1966

Untitled 1994

From **"Other Men's Flowers"**, text works by 15 London based artists, curated by Joshua Compston, and published 1994 by Charles Booth-Clibborn under his imprint The Paragon Press

Letterpress, 19.4 × 33 plate; 47 × 61 sheet
18/100

Purchased from The Paragon Press November 1994
P6300

P5520

FIELDING Brian 1933–1987
Tiger 1987

From **Artists' Choice**, a portfolio of 48 prints by 48 artists, published 1987 by the Royal College of Art Printmaking Course

Lithograph, 30.5 × 30.5 image and sheet
4/48
Purchased from the Royal College of Art Printmaking Course August 1987
P5520

FLANAGAN Barry B 1941
Loch Ness 1976

A set of six etchings
Each plate 15.5 × 23; sheet 33 × 55
Published by Bernard Jacobson 1976
Numbered 11 of an edition of 50
Purchased from Bernard Jacobson Gallery April 1984
P4854 – P4859

Loch Ness 1
P4854

Loch Ness 2
P4855

P4856

Loch Ness 3
P4856

Loch Ness 4
P4857

Loch Ness 5
P4858

Loch Ness 6
P4859

FLANAGAN Barry B 1941
Urquhart Castle 1976

Linocut, 28.4 × 52 image; 34.3 × 56.5 sheet
20/25
Purchased from Bernard Jacobson Gallery April 1984
P4860

FLANAGAN Barry B 1941
Loch Tariff 1976

Linocut, 32.5 × 32 image; 38 × 56.8 sheet
21/40
Purchased from Bernard Jacobson Gallery April 1984
P4861

FLANAGAN Barry B 1941
The Abbey 1976

Linocut, 30.5 × 49.5 image; 38 × 56 sheet
18/60
Purchased from Bernard Jacobson Gallery April 1984
P4862

FLANAGAN Barry B 1941
Passerines 1994

From **Nine London Birds**, a portfolio of nine prints by nine artists, published 1994 by the Byam Shaw School of Art
Etching and aquatint, 17.6 × 24.8 plate; 31.4 × 41 sheet
26/80
Purchased from the Byam Shaw School of Art May 1994
P6280

FREUD Lucian B 1922
Head and Shoulders 1982

Etching, 24.5 × 30 plate; 38 × 41.5 sheet
14/20
Purchased from James Kirkman Ltd., London April 1984
P4876

FREUD Lucian B 1922
Head on a Pillow 1982

Etching, 10.2 × 12.7 plate; 23 × 24.5 sheet
Artist's proof III/IV
Purchased from James Kirkman Ltd., London April 1984
P4877

FREUD Lucian B 1922
Head of a Girl I 1982

Etching, 11.2 × 11.5 plate; 27.3 × 21 sheet
Artist's proof III/IV
Purchased from James Kirkman Ltd., London April 1984
P4878

FREUD Lucian B 1922
Head of a Girl II 1982

Etching, 16.2 × 13 plate; 34.5 × 28.3 sheet
14/16
Purchased from James Kirkman Ltd., London April 1984
P4879

FRINK Elisabeth 1930–1993
I flew through a black cloud and the winds came up from the hills below me

From **Artists' Choice**, a portfolio of 48 prints by 48 artists, published 1987 by the Royal College of Art Printmaking Course

Etching, 30.5 × 30.5 image and sheet
4/48
Purchased from the Royal College of Art Printmaking Course August 1987
P5551

FROST Terry B 1915
"Oh what an effort it is to love you as I do"

(Garcia Lorca)

From **Artists' Choice**, a portfolio of 48 prints by 48 artists, published 1987 by the Royal College of Art Printmaking Course

Screenprint, 30.5 × 30.5 image and sheet
4/48
Purchased from the Royal College of Art Printmaking Course August 1987
P5514

FROST Terry B 1915
Lemon Glow 1991

From **Six Artists, The 1992 Royal College of Art Portfolio of Prints**, published by the Royal College of Art Printmaking Course
Screenprint, 56.5 × 76.5 image and sheet
26/50
Purchased from the Royal College of Art Printmaking Course March 1993
P6193   (colour plate 37)

GILLICK Liam B 1964
Untitled 1994

From **"Other Men's Flowers"**, text works by 15 London based artists, curated by Joshua Compston, and published 1994 by Charles Booth-Clibborn under his imprint The Paragon Press
Letterpress, 61 × 47 sheet
18/100
Purchased from The Paragon Press November 1994
P6301

GINGER Phyllis B 1907
Town Centre

School Print 7 from **School Prints** 1946–49, printed at The Baynard Press
Lithograph, 49.6 × 76.3 image and sheet
Purchased from Merivale Editions December 1993
P6204

GOLDING John B 1929
Essai 1987

From **Artists' Choice**, a portfolio of 48 prints by 48 artists, published 1987 by the Royal College of Art Printmaking Course

Lithograph, 21 × 29.5 image; 30.5 × 30.5 sheet
4/48
Purchased from the Royal College of Art Printmaking Course August 1987
P5527

GRANT Alistair B 1925
The Bridge at Étaples

From **Artists' Choice**, a portfolio of 48 prints by 48 artists, published 1987 by the Royal College of Art Printmaking Course

Lithograph and screenprint
30.5 × 30.5 image and sheet
4/48
Purchased from the Royal College of Art Printmaking Course August 1987
P5537

GREEN Alan B 1932
Seven Framed Images 1983

A suite of seven etchings
Image and sheet sizes vary
Published by Juda Rowan Gallery 1983
Numbered 12 of an edition of 25
Purchased from Juda Rowan Gallery September 1984
P4906 – P4912

No. 1

Two plate etching
33 × 30 each plate; 30.5 × 28 sheet
P4906

No. 2

Two plate etching and collage
21 × 21 each plate; 30 × 29.3 sheet
P4907

P4908

No. 3

Two plate etching and aquatint
22.3 × 22 each plate; 29.4 × 28.5 sheet
P4908

No. 4

Two plate etching and aquatint
18 × 16.5 each plate; 29.5 × 27.5 sheet
P4909

No. 5

Two plate etching, aquatint and collage
26 × 25 each plate; 24 × 23 sheet
P4910

No. 6

Three plate etching, drypoint and
collage, 24 × 22; 13.2 × 11.7; 9.8 × 11.7
plates; 29.5 × 27 sheet
P4911

No. 7

Two plate etching and collage
21.5 × 21.2 each plate; 28.3 × 28.3 sheet
P4912

HAMBLING Maggi B 1945
Heron 1994

From **Nine London Birds**, a portfolio of
nine prints by nine artists, published
1994 by the Byam Shaw School of Art
Aquatint and sugarlift, 29.3 × 22.2 plate;
40.8 × 30.5 sheet
26/80
Purchased from the Byam Shaw School
of Art May 1994
P6281

HAMILTON Richard B 1922
**Just what is it that makes today's
homes so different?** 1993

Laser print, 17.6 × 26.7 image;
21 × 29.7 sheet
Numbered CP19/100 from an edition of
5000 signed and numbered prints
produced for the BBC's programme
QED, shown 21 April 1993
Presented by the artist June 1993
P6179

HARDIE Gwen B 1962
I am 1987

Lithograph, 57 × 72 image and sheet
2/20
Purchased from Edinburgh
Printmakers December 1989
P5733

HARDIE Gwen B 1962
I am 1987

Lithograph, 57 × 72 image and sheet
4/20
Purchased from Edinburgh
Printmakers December 1989
P5734

HARDIE Gwen B 1962
I am 1987

Lithograph, 57 × 72 image and sheet
Artist's proof
Purchased from Edinburgh
Printmakers December 1989
P5735

HATT Christine B 1954
Plus Minus 1988

From **The Culford Press Print Folio
1988**, three prints by three artists,
published by Culford Press, London
Etching, 44.5 × 44 plate; 55.6 × 49.3 sheet
12/50
Purchased from Culford Press, London
October 1988
P5614

HEATH Adrian 1920–1992
Untitled 1983

Etching and watercolour
24.1 × 23.6 plate; 40 × 37.1 sheet
Artist's proof
Presented by Mary Waine November
1986
P5432

HEINDORFF Michael B 1949
The Baron in the Trees

From **Artists' Choice**, a portfolio of 48
prints by 48 artists, published 1987 by
the Royal College of Art Printmaking
Course
Lithograph, 30.5 × 30.5 image and sheet
4/48
Purchased from the Royal College of
Art Printmaking Course August 1987
P5542

HEMPTON Paul B 1946
Stone, Staff and Ellipse 1982

Etching, 53 × 45 plate; 89 × 70 sheet
65/100
Purchased from Anderson O'Day
Gallery July 1984
P4898

HERMAN Andrew B 1961
Untitled 1994

From "Other Men's Flowers", text
works by 15 London based artists,
curated by Joshua Compston, and
published 1994 by Charles Booth-
Clibborn under his imprint The
Paragon Press
Screenprint, 61 × 47
18/100
Purchased from The Paragon Press
November 1994
P6302

HERON Patrick B 1920
Garden Print: 1987 1987

From **Artists' Choice**, a portfolio of 48
prints by 48 artists, published 1987 by
the Royal College of Art Printmaking
Course
Lithograph, 30.5 × 30.5 image and sheet
4/48
Purchased from the Royal College of
Art Printmaking Course August 1987
P5534

HEWITT John B 1955
Big Race Winner 1987

From **Artists' Choice**, a portfolio of 48
prints by 48 artists, published 1987 by
the Royal College of Art Printmaking
Course
Etching, 30.5 × 30.5 image and sheet
4/48
Purchased from the Royal College of
Art Printmaking Course August 1987
P5533

HILTON Matthew B 1948
Object 1993

Linoprint, 21.5 × 62.8 image;
29.3 × 69.2 sheet
5/6
Purchased from the artist April 1994
P6266

HILTON Matthew B 1948
And Some (2) 1993

Linoprint, 51.2 × 75.2 image;
56 × 80 sheet
4/4
Purchased from the artist April 1994
P6267

HIRST Damien B 1965
Untitled 1992

From **London**, a portfolio of 11 prints
made by 11 artists working in London,
published 1992 by Charles Booth-
Clibborn under his imprint The
Paragon Press
Screenprint with matt varnish
86 × 62.4 image and sheet
38/65
Purchased from Karsten Schubert,
London June 1992
P6068

HOCKNEY David B 1937
The Poet 1976–77

From **The Blue Guitar**, a portfolio of 20
etchings, published 1977 by Petersburg
Press
Etching and aquatint, 34.5 × 42.5 plate;
46 × 53 sheet
120/200
Purchased from Christie's
Contemporary Art, London March 1985
P5054

HODES Charlotte B 1959
Fragments 1988

From **The Culford Press Print Folio
1988**, three prints by three artists,
published by Culford Press, London
Etching, 30 × 38 plate; 49 × 55 sheet
12/50
Purchased from Culford Press, London
October 1988
P5615

HODGKIN Howard B 1932
For Bernard Jacobson 1979

Two sheet lithograph, with hand
colouring , 105.7 × 149.9 overall image
and sheet
Artist's proof
Purchased from Bernard Jacobson
Gallery February 1985
P5010

HODGKIN Howard B 1932
Lotus 1980

Screenprint, 74 × 91.6 image and sheet
8/100
Purchased from Bernard Jacobson
Gallery February 1985
P5012

HODGKIN Howard B 1932
After Lunch 1980

Etching and aquatint, with hand
colouring, 56.4 × 76.1 image and sheet
98/100
Purchased from Petersburg Press
February 1985
P5014

P5013

HODGKIN Howard B 1932
Souvenir 1981

Screenprint, 114.3 × 139.7 image and sheet
98/100
Purchased from Petersburg Press
February 1985
P5013

HODGKIN Howard B 1932
Two to Go 1982

Lithograph, with hand colouring
91.8 × 122.6 image and sheet
8/100
Purchased from Bernard Jacobson
Gallery February 1985
P5011

HODGKIN Howard B 1932
Moroccan Door 1990–91

Hand coloured etching, with
carborundum, 76 × 111.5 image and
sheet
20/55
Purchased from Waddington Galleries
April 1991
P5928

HODGKIN Howard B 1932
Mango 1990–91

Hand coloured etching, with carborundum, 76 × 111.5 image and sheet
20/55
Purchased from Waddington Galleries April 1991
P5929

HODGKIN Howard B 1932
In an Empty Room 1990–91

Hand coloured etching, with carborundum, 120.5 × 149.5 image and sheet
20/55
Purchased from Waddington Galleries April 1991
P5930

HODGKIN Howard B 1932
Indian Tree 1990–91

Hand coloured etching, with carborundum, 92 × 121 image and sheet
20/55
Purchased from Waddington Galleries April 1991
P5931

HODGKIN Howard B 1932
Night Palm 1990–91

Hand coloured etching, with carborundum, 149.5 × 120.5 image and sheet
20/55
Purchased from Waddington Galleries April 1991
P5932

HODGKIN Howard B 1932
Street Palm 1990–91

Hand coloured etching, with carborundum, 149.5 × 120.5 image and sheet
20/55
Purchased from Waddington Galleries April 1991
P5933

HODGKIN Howard B 1932
Palm and Window 1990–91

Hand coloured etching, with carborundum, 149.5 × 120.5 image and sheet
20/55
Purchased from Waddington Galleries April 1991
P5934

HODGKIN Howard B 1932
Flowering Palm 1990–91

Hand coloured etching, with carborundum, 149.5 × 120.5 image and sheet
20/55
Purchased from Waddington Galleries April 1991
P5935

HOWSON Peter B 1958

Three screenprints, 1986, from both the book and portfolio editions of **The Scottish Bestiary**, 20 prints in various media, various sizes, by seven Scottish artists illustrating the writings in poetry and prose of George Mackay Brown
Published 1986 by Charles Booth-Clibborn under his imprint The Paragon Press in a book edition of 60 and a portfolio edition of 50
Book edition works purchased from The Paragon Press December 1986
P5453, P5465, P5467

Portfolio edition works purchased from Angela Flowers Gallery February 1987
P5479, P5480, P5481

Fieldmouse

56 × 76 sheet (image and text)
Book edition: 26/60
P5453

Moth

56 × 76 sheet (image and text)
Book edition: 26/60
P5465

Stag

56 × 76 sheet (image and text)
Book edition: 26/60
P5467

Moth

54.5 × 36.7 image; 64.5 × 45.5 sheet
Portfolio edition: 45/50
P5479

Stag

55 × 36.7 image; 64.5 × 46.1 sheet
Portfolio edition: 45/50
P5480   (colour plate 38)

Fieldmouse

55 × 36.8 image; 65.9 × 47 sheet
Portfolio edition: 45/50
P5481

HOWSON Peter B 1958
Johnie* 1987

Etching, 33 × 24.7 plate; 56 × 38 sheet
Artist's proof VI
Purchased from Edinburgh Printmakers March 1989
P5629

HOWSON Peter B 1958
Ned* 1987

Etching, 32.5 × 24.6 plate; 56.7 × 38.2 sheet
Artist's proof III
Purchased from Edinburgh Printmakers March 1989
P5630

HOWSON Peter B 1958
Maxwell* 1987

Etching, 33.3 × 24.7 plate; 56.5 × 38 sheet
Artist's proof III
Purchased from Edinburgh Printmakers March 1989
P5631

HOWSON Peter B 1958
Peter* 1987

Etching, 32.5 × 24.8 plate; 56.5 × 38 sheet
Artist's proof VI
Purchased from Edinburgh Printmakers March 1989
P5632

*Printed by Edinburgh Printmakers, subsequently published 1988 by Flowers Graphics as part of **Saracen Heads**, a portfolio of 25 etchings in an edition of 40 (including 10 portfolios which contain an original drawing)

HOWSON Peter B 1958
The Heroic Dosser 1987

Woodcut, two sheets joined
177 × 116 overall image;
182 × 120.5 overall sheet
24/30
Purchased from Angela Flowers Gallery March 1990
P5804

HOWSON Peter B 1958
The Noble Dosser 1987

Woodcut, two sheets joined
177.4 × 116.7 overall image;
182 × 120.5 overall sheet
12/30
Purchased from Angela Flowers Gallery March 1990
P5805

HOWSON Peter B 1958
The Bodybuilder 1988

Screenprint, 150 × 101 image;
151 × 107 sheet
5/30
Purchased from the artist November 1988
P5616

HOWSON Peter B 1958
The Noble Dosser 1988

Screenprint, 150 × 102 image;
151 × 107 sheet
This print is not inscribed with an edition number
Purchased from the artist November 1988
P5617

HOWSON Peter B 1958
The Heroic Dosser 1988

Screenprint, 150 × 102 image;
151 × 107 sheet
This print is not inscribed with an edition number
Purchased from the artist November 1988
P5618

HOYLAND John B 1934
Galaxy

From **Artists' Choice**, a portfolio of 48 prints by 48 artists, published 1987 by the Royal College of Art Printmaking Course
Linocut, 29.5 × 27.5 image;
30.5 × 30.5 sheet
4/48
Purchased from the Royal College of Art Printmaking Course August 1987
P5549

HOYLAND John B 1934

Three etchings and aquatints, 1989, from **John Hoyland, a series of eight etchings and aquatints**
Published 1989 by Waddington Graphics in an edition of 65
Purchased from Waddington Galleries January 1992
P6009 – P6011

Banda Oriental

63.5 × 49.3 plate; 90.3 × 69.5 sheet
3/65
P6009

Captive Circle

63.5 × 50 plate; 90 × 69.5 sheet
3/65
P6010

Sun Animal

64 × 49.3 plate; 90.2 × 69.6 sheet
3/65
P6011

HSIUNG Kai-Lu B 1964
Avarice 1988

Screenprint, 107 × 77 image;
114.2 × 83.7 sheet
8/9
Purchased from the artist December 1989
P5766

HUME Gary B 1962
Untitled 1994

From **"Other Men's Flowers"**, text works by 15 London based artists, curated by Joshua Compston, and published 1994 by Charles Booth-Clibborn under his imprint The Paragon Press
Screenprint, 31.8 × 42 image;
47 × 61 sheet
18/100
Purchased from The Paragon Press November 1994
P6303

HUTTON Clarke 1898–1984
Harlequinade

School Print 13 from **School Prints** 1946–49, printed at The Baynard Press
Lithograph, 49.3 × 75.8 image and sheet
Purchased from Merivale Editions December 1993
P6206

IRVIN Albert B 1922
Battle Bridge 1980

From **The London Suite**, 1982, a set of ten screenprints by ten London based artists, published by Advanced Graphics, London in an edition of 75
Screenprint, 44.5 × 59 image; 61 × 78.5 sheet
Artist's proof
Purchased from Anderson O'Day Gallery June 1984
P4880

IRVIN Albert B 1922
Abbots 1983

Screenprint, 33 × 48 image; 47 × 61.5 sheet
20/100
Purchased from Anderson O'Day Gallery June 1984
P4881

IRVIN Albert B 1922
Druid I 1984

Screenprint, 156 × 128.5 image and sheet
28/35
Purchased from Anderson O'Day Gallery October 1984
P4959

IRVIN Albert B 1922
Druid II 1984

Screenprint, 156 × 128.5 image and sheet
28/35
Purchased from Anderson O'Day Gallery October 1984
P4960

IRVIN Albert B 1922
Magdalen 1986

Screenprint, 91.5 × 119 image; 106 × 132 sheet
71/125
Purchased from Gimpel Fils August 1987
P5562

IRVIN Albert B 1922
"The poet or painter steers his life to maim . . ." 1987

From **Artists' Choice**, a portfolio of 48 prints by 48 artists, published 1987 by the Royal College of Art Printmaking Course
Screenprint, 25.5 × 26 image; 30.5 × 30.5 sheet
4/48
Purchased from the Royal College of Art Printmaking Course August 1987
P5517

IRVIN Albert B 1922
Prince Consort 1995

From **Six Artists, The 1994 Royal College of Art Portfolio of Prints**, published by the Royal College of Art Printmaking Course (portfolio completed 1995)
Screenprint, 57 × 76.2 image and sheet
26/50
Purchased from The Royal College of Art Printmaking Course June 1994
P6310

JACKLIN Bill B 1943
Woman in a Chair

From **Artists' Choice**, a portfolio of 48 prints by 48 artists, published 1987 by the Royal College of Art Printmaking Course
Etching, 17.8 × 13.3 plate; 30.5 × 30.5 sheet
4/48
Purchased from the Royal College of Art Printmaking Course August 1987
P5539

JONES Allen B 1937
Stage Set 1982

Lithograph in four parts
56.5 × 76.2 each part; 113 × 152.4 overall size
Stage Set consists of four lithographs which can be hung separately or in pairs, vertically and horizontally, yet can be placed altogether in one large composition
56/75
Purchased from Waddington Galleries February 1985
P5005 A–D

JONES Allen B 1937
Grenada

From **Artists' Choice**, a portfolio of 48 prints by 48 artists, published 1987 by the Royal College of Art Printmaking Course
Etching, 19.6 × 20 plate; 30.5 × 30.5 sheet
4/48
Purchased from the Royal College of Art Printmaking Course August 1987
P5543

JONES Barbara 1912–1978
Fairground

School Print 2 from **School Prints** 1946–49, printed at The Baynard Press
Lithograph, 51.2 × 76 image and sheet
Purchased from Merivale Editions December 1993
P6200 (colour plate 39)

KALORKOTI Panayiotis B 1957
The Fathers of Modern Art 1984

A series of eight etchings
Each sheet 56.5 × 67.3; plate sizes vary
Published by the artist 1984
Numbered 10 of an edition of 50
Purchased from the artist October 1987
P5566 – P5573

Seurat

35 × 49.5 plate
P5566

Cézanne

34.7 × 49.2 plate
P5567

Whistler

34.4 × 49.5 plate
P5568

Picasso

34.3 × 49 plate
P5569

Matisse

32.5 × 49 plate
P5570

Klee

35 × 49.7 plate
P5571

Pollock

36.5 × 49.7 plate
P5572

De Kooning

34.5 × 49 plate
P5573

KALORKOTI Panayiotis B 1957
Untitled/Composition 1987

Etching, 35 × 49.8 plate; 56.5 × 76.2 sheet
4/10
Presented by the artist October 1987
P5574

KALORKOTI Panayiotis B 1957
The Two Friends 1987

Etching, 35 × 49.7 plate; 56.5 × 76.2 sheet
7/10
Presented by the artist October 1987
P5575

KALORKOTI Panayiotis B 1957
An Artist's Studio 1987

Etching, 35 × 49.1 plate; 56.5 × 76.2 sheet
5/10
Presented by the artist October 1987
P5576

KIFF Ken B 1935
The Sun shining down on a Street

From **Artists' Choice**, a portfolio of 48 prints by 48 artists, published 1987 by the Royal College of Art Printmaking Course
Drypoint, 27.5 × 23.5 plate; 30.5 × 30.5 sheet
4/48
Purchased from the Royal College of Art Printmaking Course August 1987
P5557

KNOX Jack B 1936

Three lithographs and screenprints, 1986, from **The Scottish Bestiary**, 20 prints in various media, various sizes, by seven Scottish artists illustrating the writings in poetry and prose of George Mackay Brown
Published 1986 by Charles Booth-Clibborn under his imprint The Paragon Press in a book edition of 60 and a portfolio edition of 50
Purchased from The Paragon Press December 1986
P5453A, P5458, P5463

Dove

56 × 76 sheet (image and text)
Book edition: 26/60
P5453A

Nuckelavee

56 × 76 sheet (image and text)
Book edition: 26/60
P5458

Whale

56 × 76 sheet (image and text)
Book edition: 26/60
P5463

P5727

KONDRACKI Henry B 1953
Partners on Ice 1988

Etching, 30.2 × 22.5 plate; 75.5 × 37.2 sheet
3/10
Purchased from Vanessa Devereux Gallery November 1989
P5727

Kondracki Henry B 1953
Bed time 1988

Etching, 30.2 × 22.5 plate;
75.5 × 37.2 sheet
1/10
Purchased from Vanessa Devereux
Gallery November 1989
P5728

Kondracki Henry B 1953
Soul Man 1988

Etching, 30.2 × 22.5 plate;
75.5 × 37.2 sheet
4/10
Purchased from Vanessa Devereux
Gallery November 1989
P5729

Kondracki Henry B 1953
Shoot out 1988

Etching, 22.5 × 30.2 plate;
37.2 × 75.5 sheet
6/10
Purchased from Vanessa Devereux
Gallery November 1989
P5730

Kondracki Henry B 1953
Playground 1989

Etching, 37.8 × 29.6 plate;
75.5 × 56.2 sheet
1/25
Purchased from Vanessa Devereux
Gallery February 1990
P5767

Kunath Rosalind B 1946
3 Dreed 1995

From **Six Artists, The 1994 Royal
College of Art Portfolio of Prints**,
published by the Royal College of Art
Printmaking Course (portfolio
completed 1995)
Computer initiated screenprint
57.4 × 76.1 image and sheet
26/50
Purchased from The Royal College of
Art Printmaking Course June 1994
P6311

La Dell Edwin 1919–1970
The Tower of London 1946

School Print 6 from **School Prints**
1946–49, printed at The Baynard Press
Lithograph, 49.9 × 76.5 image and sheet
Purchased from Merivale Editions
December 1993
P6203

Lamb Elspeth B 1951
Moonsong at Morning 1986

Lithograph in two parts
86.2 × 58.8 image and sheet;
56.7 × 76 image and sheet
iv/vi
Purchased from Art in Business,
Edinburgh September 1987
P5564

P6070

Landy Michael B 1963
COR! WHAT A BARGAIN! 1992

From **London**, a portfolio of 11 prints
made by 11 artists working in London,
published 1992 by Charles Booth-
Clibborn under his imprint The
Paragon Press
Screenprint, laminated in plastic, with
black marker-pen
68.5 × 85.7 image and sheet
38/65
Purchased from Karsten Schubert,
London June 1992
P6070

Langlands & Bell
Langlands Ben B 1955
Bell Nikki B 1959
UNO City 1992

From **London**, a portfolio of 11 prints
made by 11 artists working in London,
published 1992 by Charles Booth-
Clibborn under his imprint The
Paragon Press
Blind embossed print
71 × 74 image and sheet
38/65
Purchased from Karsten Schubert,
London June 1992
P6069

McLean Bruce B 1944
**A Certain Smile (A New Front
Door?)** 1980

Screenprint, 99 × 114 image;
101.4 × 123.5 sheet
3/50
Purchased from Glasgow Print Studio
February 1985
P5008

McLean Bruce B 1944
**A Certain Smile (A New Front
Door?)** 1980

Screenprint, 99 × 114 image;
101.4 × 123.5 sheet
5/50
Purchased from Glasgow Print Studio
February 1985
P5009

McLean Bruce B 1944
Pot Head Man 1984

Screenprint, 67 × 96 image;
70 × 100 sheet
3/30
Purchased from Angela Flowers Gallery
March 1990
P5759

McLean Bruce B 1944
Jazz at The Bull 1985

Screenprint, 101.5 × 76 image and sheet
9/35
Purchased from Angela Flowers Gallery
January 1990
P5758

McLean Bruce B 1944
Blue Splash, Red Door 1986

Lithograph, 87 × 71.5 image;
113 × 77 sheet
3/25
Purchased from Northern Print,
Newcastle upon Tyne July 1986
P5410

McLean Bruce B 1944
A Spot of Unpleasant Bending
1986

Lithograph, 85 × 69.5 image;
113 × 77 sheet
3/25
Purchased from Northern Print,
Newcastle upon Tyne July 1986
P5411

McLean Bruce B 1944
She Sleeps with a Jug 1986

Lithograph, 85 × 70.5 image;
113 × 77 sheet
3/25
Purchased from Northern Print,
Newcastle upon Tyne July 1986
P5412

McLean Bruce B 1944
Blue Pipe Smoker 1986

Lithograph, 87 × 70.5 image;
113 × 77 sheet
3/25
Purchased from Northern Print,
Newcastle upon Tyne July 1986
P5413

McLean Bruce B 1944
Three screenprints, 1986, from **The
Scottish Bestiary**, 20 prints in various
media, various sizes, by seven Scottish
artists illustrating the writings in poetry
and prose of George Mackay Brown
Published 1986 by Charles Booth-
Clibborn under his imprint The
Paragon Press in a book edition of 60
and a portfolio edition of 50
Purchased from The Paragon Press
December 1986
P5455, P5456, P5460

Spider

56 × 76 sheet (image and text)
Book edition: 26/60
P5455

Salmon

56 × 76 sheet (image and text)
Book edition: 26/60
P5456

Stoor-Worm

56 × 76 sheet (image and text)
Book edition: 26/60
P5460

McLean Bruce B 1944
Hot Slick 1989

From **King's Fund Prints**, a set of six
prints chosen by Richard Cork,
published 1989 by The King's Fund
in an edition of 250
Screenprint, 101.2 × 127.4 image;
119.8 × 149.6 sheet
243/250
Purchased from The Scottish Gallery,
London January 1990
P5756 (colour plate 40)

Mara Tim B 1948
The Black Series

An open-ended grouping of
screenprints
Standard sheet size: portrait 91 × 63;
landscape 63 × 91
Published by the artist from 1985
onwards
Editions of 15
P6086, P6087, P6088, P6089, P6093,
P6315

Coal and Diamonds 1985

91 × 63 image and sheet
12/15
Purchased from the artist December
1994
P6315 (colour plate 41)

Stacking Chairs 1986

91 × 63 image and sheet
10/15
Purchased from the artist August 1992
P6086

Stool with Press 1986

91 × 63 image and sheet
7/15
Purchased from the artist August 1992
P6089

New Broom 1987

91 × 63 image and sheet
3/15
Presented by the artist September 1992
P6093

Helping Hands 1989

63 × 91 image and sheet
13/15
Purchased from the artist August 1992
P6087

Bust 1989

63 × 91 image and sheet
11/15
Purchased from the artist August 1992
P6088

Mara Tim B 1948
The Black Room 1987

From **Artists' Choice**, a portfolio of 48
prints by 48 artists, published 1987 by
the Royal College of Art Printmaking
Course
Screenprint, 30.5 × 30.5 image and sheet
4/48
Purchased from the Royal College of
Art Printmaking Course August 1987
P5547

MARA Tim B 1948
The Journal 1987

Screenprint, 91 × 120.5 image and sheet
3/20
Purchased from Angela Flowers Gallery
December 1989
P5746

MARA Tim B 1948
Plastic Funnel, Mortar and Pestle
1992

From **Six Artists, The 1992 Royal
College of Art Portfolio of Prints**,
published by the Royal College of Art
Printmaking Course
Screenprint, 76 × 57 image and sheet
26/50
Purchased from the Royal College of
Art Printmaking Course March 1993
P6190

MATTHEWS Peter B 1942
River 1981

Etching and aquatint, 34 × 46.5 plate;
59.5 × 78.3 sheet
40/50
Purchased from Anderson O'Day
Gallery July 1984
P4894

MATTHEWS Peter B 1942
Wooded Rock 1981

Etching and aquatint, 49.5 × 33 plate;
75 × 57 sheet
38/50
Purchased from Anderson O'Day
Gallery July 1984
P4896

MATTHEWS Peter B 1942
Heather Moor 1982

Etching and aquatint, 27.5 × 33.5 plate;
55 × 57 sheet
Artist's proof
Purchased from Anderson O'Day
Gallery July 1984
P4893

MATTHEWS Peter B 1942
Northern Stack 1982

Etching and aquatint, 34.5 × 49.5 plate;
53.5 × 68.5 sheet
8/50
Purchased from Anderson O'Day
Gallery July 1984
P4895

MATTHEWS Peter B 1942
Evening Sea 1983

Etching and aquatint, 38.5 × 48.5 plate;
57 × 75 sheet
19/50
Purchased from Anderson O'Day
Gallery July 1984
P4891

MATTHEWS Peter B 1942
Hinterland 1984

Etching and aquatint, 35 × 48 plate;
59.5 × 78 sheet
19/75
Purchased from Anderson O'Day
Gallery July 1984
P4892

MAY Nicholas B 1962
Anabatic Print 1992

From **London**, a portfolio of 11 prints
made by 11 artists working in London,
published 1992 by Charles Booth-
Clibborn under his imprint The
Paragon Press
Screenprint with high gloss varnish
75 × 47 image; 88.5 × 60 sheet
38/65
Purchased from Karsten Schubert,
London June 1992
P6071

MOORE Henry 1898–1986
Sculptural Objects 1949

School Print 30 from **School Prints**
1946–49, printed at The Baynard Press
Lithograph, 49.5 × 76.2 image and sheet
CGM 7
Presented anonymously November 1992
P6099

MOORE Henry 1898–1986
THE HENRY MOORE GIFT

In 1984 Henry Moore, through the
offices of the Henry Moore Foundation,
gave the British Council over two
hundred of his finest prints as a fiftieth
anniversary present. Upon donating his
gift, Moore wrote, "It gives me much
pleasure to present these works for the
British Council's 50th birthday. My
graphic work has often been an
introduction to many people who have
gone on to look at sculpture. I am very
pleased they will now be out on
exhibition with the British Council,
being seen by so many people around
the world."
This generous gift, which covers most
periods of the artist's work from the
1940s, was selected to complement the
British Council's existing collection of
one hundred and twenty four Moore
prints. The majority of the works were
presented and accessioned by
November 1985. An additional
portfolio, **Mother and Child**, was
donated in October 1989.
Note on the entries
Works are listed chronologically and in
British Council Collection accession
number sequence. With the exception
of four portfolios – **Elephant Skull
Album, La Poésie, The Henry Moore
80th Anniversary Portfolio**, and
Animals in the Zoo – this listing
accords with the published portfolio
order. For ease of reference, therefore,
works from these portfolios now also
observe strict portfolio order,
irrespective of date and British Council
Collection accession number.

Also cited are the catalogue numbers
(CGM) from the Catalogue Raisonné,
*Henry Moore: Catalogue of Graphic
Work*, published in four volumes
(Cramer, Geneva 1973-1986).
Edition numbers are not given, as so
many of the prints are designated
artist's copies or hors commerce. Many
are inscribed 'For B.C. Henry Moore'.

MOORE Henry 1898–1986
Figures in Settings 1949

Collograph, 57.5 × 40 image
CGM 5, P5070

P5077

MOORE Henry 1898–1986
Standing Figures 1949

Collograph, 37.8 × 47 image
CGM 9, P5077

MOORE Henry 1898–1986
Woman Holding Cat 1949

Collograph, 29.8 × 48.9 image
CGM 10, P5085

MOORE Henry 1898–1986
Hommage à Rodin 1966

Lithograph, 29.5 × 23.5 image
CGM 59, P5073

MOORE Henry 1898–1986
**Six Reclining Figures on Green
Ground** 1966

Lithograph, 33.6 × 28.6 image
CGM 61, P5076

MOORE Henry 1898–1986
**Three Reclining Figures on
Pedestals** 1966

Lithograph, 30.5 × 26.7 image
CGM 62, P5080

MOORE Henry 1898–1986
Four Draped Reclining Figures
1967

Etching, 14.9 × 21.6 plate
CGM 90, P5071

MOORE Henry 1898–1986
Reclining Figure 1967

Lithograph, 11.4 × 16.8 image
CGM 100, P5075

MOORE Henry 1898–1986
Eight etchings from **Elephant Skull
Album** 1969–70
Published 1970 by Gérald Cramer,
Geneva in an edition of 100
P5062 – P5069

Elephant Skull Plate II 1969

Etching, 22.5 × 19.7 plate
CGM 115, P5063

Elephant Skull Plate IV 1969

Etching and drypoint, 22.2 × 23.8 plate
CGM 117, P5064

Elephant Skull Plate VI 1970

Etching and drypoint, 20 × 29.8 plate
CGM 119, P5065

Elephant Skull Plate XVI 1970

Etching, 34.6 × 24.8 plate
CGM 129, P5066

Elephant Skull Plate XIX 1969

Etching, 23.5 × 30.8 plate
CGM 132, P5067

Elephant Skull Plate XXIV 1970

Etching and drypoint, 20 × 29.8 plate
CGM 137, P5068

Elephant Skull Plate C 1969

Etching and drypoint, 21.9 × 20 plate
CGM 144, P5069

Elephant Skull: Arch Form 1970

Etching, 14.9 × 11.4 plate
CGM 147, P5062

MOORE Henry 1898–1986
Storm at Sea 1970

Etching and drypoint, 13.3 × 23.5 plate
CGM 156, P5078

MOORE Henry 1898–1986
Three Sculpture Motives 1970

Etching, 29.5 × 19.7 plate
CGM 158, P5081

MOORE Henry 1898–1986
Two Standing Figures No. V 1970

Etching, 30.8 × 23.8 plate
CGM 160, P5084

MOORE Henry 1898–1986
Wreck 1970

Etching and drypoint, 13.7 × 23.5 plate
CGM 162, P5086

MOORE Henry 1898–1986
Four Sculpture Motives 1971

Etching and aquatint, 20.3 × 16.5 plate
CGM 170, P5072

MOORE Henry 1898–1986
Three Reclining Figures 1971

Lithograph, 29.8 × 22.9 image
CGM 183, P5079

MOORE Henry 1898–1986
Tunnel, Arch and Window 1971

Etching, aquatint and drypoint
15.2 × 15.2 plate
CGM 174, P5082

MOORE Henry 1898–1986
Turning Figure No. 1 1971

Etching, 23.5 × 13.7 plate
CGM 175, P5083

MOORE Henry 1898–1986
Architecture: Doorway 1972

Etching, aquatint and drypoint
19.1 × 21.3 plate
CGM 185, P5061

P5074

MOORE Henry 1898–1986
Log Pile II 1972

Etching, 20.6 × 19.1 plate
CGM 190, P5074

MOORE Henry 1898–1986
Four Reclining Figures 1973

Lithograph, 41.9 × 62.2 image
CGM 282, P5089

MOORE Henry 1898–1986
Landscape 1973

Lithograph, 21.6 × 29.2 image
CGM 287, P5097

MOORE Henry 1898–1986
Mother and Child 1973

Lithograph, 24.2 × 17.5 image
CGM 288, P5101

P5112

MOORE Henry 1898–1986
Two Women Bathing Child II 1973

Lithograph, 36.9 × 42.2 image
CGM 310, P5112

MOORE Henry 1898–1986
11 lithographs from the book
edition, and eight lithographs from the
portfolio edition of **Auden Poems ·
Moore Lithographs** 1973
Published 1974 by Petersburg Press in a
book edition totalling 330 and a
portfolio edition of 75
P5142 – P5160

Windswept Landscape

41.3 × 33.7 image
Book edition
CGM 245, P5142

Garsdale

24.8 × 31.7 image
Book edition
CGM 246, P5143

Cavern

32.1 × 26.7 image
Book edition
CGM 248, P5144

Lullaby Sleeping Head

27.3 × 29.2 image
Book edition
CGM 250, P5145

Multitude II

29.2 × 27 image
Book edition
CGM 253, P5146

Thin-Lipped Armourer II

21.6 × 29.2 image
Book edition
CGM 254, P5147

Divided Landscape

41.3 × 34 image
Book edition
CGM 256, P5148

Split Stone

30.2 × 15 image
Book edition
CGM 259, P5149

Fjord

22.2 × 25.4 image
Book edition
CGM 260, P5150

The Forest

28.9 × 21 image
Book edition
CGM 262, P5151

Sketches of Auden

28 × 21.6 image
Book edition
CGM 265, P5152

Portfolio Folder

45.1 × 25.4 image
Portfolio edition
CGM 266, P5153

Multitude I

28.3 × 22.5 image
Portfolio edition
CGM 267, P5154

Thin-Lipped Armourer I

22.5 × 29.5 image
Portfolio edition
CGM 268, P5155

Two Heads

12.7 × 20 image
Portfolio edition
CGM 269, P5156

Lullaby Sketches

24.2 × 17.5 image
Portfolio edition
CGM 270, P5157

Lullaby

28.9 × 30.5 image
Portfolio edition
CGM 271, P5158

Man and Woman

36.2 × 26 image
Portfolio edition
CGM 272, P5159

Bridge

24.8 × 34.3 image
Portfolio edition
CGM 273, P5160

MOORE Henry 1898–1986
Three Heads 1973

Lithograph, 10.8 × 15.9 image
CGM 376, P5212

MOORE Henry 1898–1986
11 lithographs from **La Poésie** 1973–75
Published 1976 by Art et Poésie, Paris in
an edition of 40
P5087, P5088, P5090, P5096, P5098,
P5099, P5100, P5103, P5109, P5110,
P5111

La Poésie 1974

15.6 × 31.1 image
CGM 315, P5098

La Poésie 1974

18.8 × 33 image
CGM 316, P5099

Les Poètes 1974

11.4 × 37.2 image
CGM 317, P5100

Two Heads 1973

11.4 × 19 image
CGM 318, P5111

Petals 1974

47.7 × 38.7 image
CGM 319, P5103 (colour plate 42)

Three Sculptural Forms 1973

51.4 × 40.7 image
CGM 320, P5110

Creole Lady 1973

54.5 × 49 image
CGM 321, P5087

Femme Allongée 1973

54 × 49 image
CGM 322, P5088

Four Standing Figures 1973

50.5 × 38 image
CGM 323, P5090

Ideas from a Sketchbook 1973

49.5 × 38.1 image
CGM 324, P5096

Three Reclining Figures 1973

50.8 × 38.5 image
CGM 325, P5109

MOORE Henry 1898–1986
Girl Seated at Desk I 1974

Lithograph, 21.9 × 15.9 image
CGM 337, P5091

P5092

MOORE Henry 1898–1986
Girl Seated at Desk II 1974

Lithograph, 25.1 × 17.8 image
CGM 338, P5092

MOORE Henry 1898–1986
Girl Seated at Desk IV 1974

Lithograph, 23 × 18.4 image
CGM 340, P5093

MOORE Henry 1898–1986
Nude 1974

Lithograph, 28 × 24.1 image
CGM 344, P5102

MOORE Henry 1898–1986
Sheep Grazing 1974

Lithograph, 12.7 × 19 image
CGM 349, P5106

MOORE Henry 1898–1986
Sheep Resting 1974

Lithograph, 12.7 × 24.8 image
CGM 350, P5107

MOORE Henry 1898–1986
Sheep Standing 1974
Lithograph, 14 × 19 image
CGM 351, P5108

MOORE Henry 1898–1986
Girl Seated at Desk VII 1974
Lithograph, 24.5 × 17.5 image
CGM 384, P5131

MOORE Henry 1898–1986
Reclining Figure 1974
Lithograph, 16 × 23.8 image
CGM 387, P5171

MOORE Henry 1898–1986
Seated Figures 1974
An album of six lithographs
Each sheet 49.5 × 42.5; image sizes vary
Published by Henry Moore, Much
Hadham 1976
Edition of 50
P5190–P5195

Seated Figure I: Line Drawing
21.6 × 15.6 image
CGM 407, P5190

P5191

Seated Figure II: Pink Background
23.4 × 15.8 image
CGM 408, P5191

Seated Figure III: Dark Room
24.1 × 17.1 image
CGM 409, P5192

Seated Figure IV: Reverse Lighting
21.6 × 14.3 image
CGM 410, P5193

Seated Figure V: Wickerwork Chair
22.2 × 16.8 image
CGM 411, P5194

Seated Figure VI: Alcove Corner
25.4 × 21.6 image
CGM 412, P5195

MOORE Henry 1898–1986
Seated Figure Holding Glass 1974
Lithograph, 11.1 × 15.2 image
CGM 388, P5196

P5200

MOORE Henry 1898–1986
Sheep before Shearing 1974
Lithograph, 20 × 28.2 image
CGM 391, P5200

MOORE Henry 1898–1986
Sheep in Field 1974
Lithograph, 19 × 27.7 image
CGM 392, P5201

MOORE Henry 1898–1986
Sheep in Stormy Landscape 1974
Lithograph, 19.5 × 28 image
CGM 393, P5202

MOORE Henry 1898–1986
Three Grazing Sheep 1974
Lithograph, 13.3 × 24.2 image
CGM 394, P5211

MOORE Henry 1898–1986
Sheep in Landscape 1974
Lithograph, 22.2 × 26 image
CGM 558, P5234

MOORE Henry 1898–1986
Head 1975
Lithograph, 43.7 × 35.6 image
CGM 364, P5094

MOORE Henry 1898–1986
Ideas for Sculptures 1975
Lithograph, 25.4 × 35 image
CGM 365, P5095

MOORE Henry 1898–1986
Reclining Figures on Beach 1975
Etching, 17.2 × 22.5 plate
CGM 363, P5104

MOORE Henry 1898–1986
Seated Mother and Child 1975
Lithograph, 29.8 × 22.2 image
CGM 367, P5105

MOORE Henry 1898–1986
Animal Heads 1975
Lithograph, 21.6 × 26.4 image
CGM 415, P5113

MOORE Henry 1898–1986
Friday Night: Camden Town 1975
Lithograph, 29.2 × 29.6 image
CGM 417, P5130

MOORE Henry 1898–1986
Group in Industrial Landscape
1975
Lithograph, 16.8 × 21.3 image
CGM 418, P5132

MOORE Henry 1898–1986
Reclining Woman 1975
Lithograph, 13 × 18.8 image
CGM 419, P5188

MOORE Henry 1898–1986
Three Reclining Figures 1975
Lithograph, 30.5 × 22.9 image
CGM 420, P5213

MOORE Henry 1898–1986
Three Seated Figures in Setting
1975
Lithograph, 22 × 35.3 image
CGM 421, P5215

MOORE Henry 1898–1986
Six lithographs, 1976, from **The Henry Moore 80th Anniversary Portfolio** 1975–76
Published 1978 by Orde Levinson,
London in an edition of 50
P5169, P5227, P5229, P5230, P5231,
P5232

Woman with Book
20.3 × 14 image
CGM 442, P5230

Woman with Arms Crossed
15.4 × 18.3 image
CGM 443, P5229

Woman with Clasped Hands
14.2 × 17.9 image
CGM 444, P5231

Two Seated Figures against Pillar
13.4 × 22.9 image
CGM 445, P5227

Woman with Dove
27.9 × 20.6 image
CGM 446, P5232

Mother and Child with Wave Background I
17.5 × 26.4 image
CGM 447, P5169

MOORE Henry 1898–1986
Figures in Snow 1976
Lithograph, 34.3 × 25.1 image
CGM 428, P5125

MOORE Henry 1898–1986
Figures with Smoke Background
1976
Lithograph, 34.3 × 25.1 image
CGM 429, P5126

MOORE Henry 1898–1986
Four Reclining Figures with Architectural Background 1976
Lithograph, 21.9 × 35.3 image
CGM 430, P5128

MOORE Henry 1898–1986
Mother and Child: Shell 1976
Lithograph, 32.1 × 25.1 image
CGM 432, P5166

MOORE Henry 1898–1986
Mother and Child with Dark Background 1976
Lithograph, 33.7 × 34.3 image
CGM 434, P5168

MOORE Henry 1898–1986
Seated Mother and Child 1976
Lithograph, 26 × 21.6 image
CGM 437, P5198

P5214

MOORE Henry 1898–1986
Three Reclining Figures on Pedestals 1976
Lithograph, 57 × 77.7 image
CGM 439, P5214

MOORE Henry 1898–1986
Two Reclining Figures 1976
Lithograph, 24 × 29 image
CGM 440, P5222

MOORE Henry 1898–1986
Two Seated Figures with Children
1976
Lithograph, 21.9 × 26.7 image
CGM 441, P5228

MOORE Henry 1898–1986
Dante Stones 1977
An album of five etchings
Each sheet 54.3 × 41.3; plate 29.2 × 19.7
Published by Raymond Spencer
Company Ltd. for the Henry Moore
Foundation, Much Hadham 1980
Edition of 50
P5117–P5121

Stone I
Etching
CGM 461, P5117

Stone II
Etching and aquatint
CGM 462, P5118

P5119

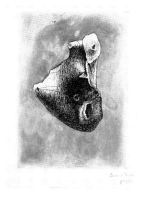

Stone III

Etching and aquatint
CGM 463, P5119

Stone IV

Etching and aquatint
CGM 464, P5120

Stone V

Etching and aquatint
CGM 465, P5121

P5167

MOORE Henry 1898–1986
Mother and Child Studies and Reclining Figure 1977

Lithograph, 38.2 × 31 image
CGM 452, P5167

MOORE Henry 1898–1986
Reclining Figure and Mother and Child Studies 1977

Lithograph, 38.2 × 30.8 image
CGM 453, P5173

MOORE Henry 1898–1986
Reclining Figure: Architectural Background I 1977

Lithograph, 31.7 × 40.7 image
CGM 454, P5174

MOORE Henry 1898–1986
Reclining Figure: Architectural Background III 1977

Lithograph, 24.8 × 30.5 image
CGM 456, P5175

MOORE Henry 1898–1986
Reclining Figure: Architectural Background IV 1977

Lithograph, 31.7 × 38.1 image
CGM 457, P5176

MOORE Henry 1898–1986
Reclining Figure: Interior Setting I 1977

Lithograph, 24.4 × 31.7 image
CGM 458, P5181

MOORE Henry 1898–1986
Reclining Figure: Interior Setting II 1977

Lithograph, 23.8 × 30.8 image
CGM 459, P5182

MOORE Henry 1898–1986
Male Figure in Landscape 1977–78

Lithograph, 23.7 × 29.2 image
CGM 470, P5163

MOORE Henry 1898–1986
Two Reclining Figures 1977–78

Etching, 30.2 × 22.5 plate
CGM 466, P5223

MOORE Henry 1898–1986
Two Reclining Figures 1977–78

Etching and aquatint, 30.2 × 22.5 plate
CGM 467, P5224

MOORE Henry 1898–1986
Two Reclining Figures 1977–78

Etching, 30.5 × 22.9 plate
CGM 468, P5225

MOORE Henry 1898–1986
Four Standing Figures 1978

Lithograph, 31.1 × 38.4 image
CGM 489, P5129

MOORE Henry 1898–1986
Sculptures in Landscape 1978

A set of four lithographs accompanying the first 200 copies of the Norwegian edition of the book *Henry Moore: Sculptures in Landscape*
Image sizes vary
Published by J M Stenersens Forlag AS, Oslo 1978
Edition of 50
P5172, P5179, P5187, P5205

Reclining Figure against Sea and Rocks

23.8 × 35.3 image
CGM 491, P5172

Reclining Figure: Dawn

22.9 × 30.8 image
CGM 492, P5179

Reclining Figure: Sunset

23.4 × 30.7 image
CGM 493, P5187 (colour plate 43)

Standing Figure: Storm Sky

24.9 × 32.7 image
CGM 494, P5205

MOORE Henry 1898–1986
Two Reclining Figures 1978

Lithograph, 26.4 × 21.9 image
CGM 497, P5226

P5854

MOORE Henry 1898–1986
Reclining Nude II 1978

Etching, 14.7 × 20 plate
CGM 483, P5854

MOORE Henry 1898–1986
Child Study 1979

Etching and drypoint, 25.1 × 18.8 plate
CGM 498, P5114

MOORE Henry 1898–1986
Curved Reclining Figure in Landscape I 1979

Etching and drypoint, 18.4 × 25.4 plate
CGM 500, P5115

MOORE Henry 1898–1986
Curved Reclining Figure in Landscape II 1979

Etching and drypoint, 18.8 × 25.4 plate
CGM 501, P5116

MOORE Henry 1898–1986
Elephants 1979

Etching, 15.2 × 20 plate
CGM 502, P5122

MOORE Henry 1898–1986
Female Torso and Sculpture Ideas I 1979

Lithograph, 28.3 × 40.3 image
CGM 534, P5123

MOORE Henry 1898–1986
Female Torso and Sculpture Ideas II 1979

Lithograph, 28.3 × 40.3 image
CGM 535, P5124

MOORE Henry 1898–1986
Five Reclining Figures 1979

Lithograph, 27.9 × 43.5 image
CGM 536, P5127

MOORE Henry 1898–1986
Head of Girl I 1979

Etching and drypoint, 22.9 × 16.5 plate
CGM 504, P5133

MOORE Henry 1898–1986
Head of Girl II 1979

Etching and drypoint, 25.4 × 18.8 plate
CGM 505, P5134

MOORE Henry 1898–1986
Head of Girl and Reclining Figure 1979

Etching, 23.2 × 27.7 plate
CGM 506, P5161

MOORE Henry 1898–1986
Homage to Sacheverell Sitwell 1979

Lithograph printed on a reproduction of a drawing, 27.3 × 19.4 image
CGM 537, P5162

MOORE Henry 1898–1986
Man and Woman 1979

Lithograph, 22.9 × 33 image
CGM 538, P5164

MOORE Henry 1898–1986
Mother and Child 1979

Etching and drypoint, 27.9 × 22.5 plate
CGM 508, P5165

MOORE Henry 1898–1986
Opening Form I 1979

Lithograph, 27 × 34.3 image
CGM 539, P5170

MOORE Henry 1898–1986
Reclining Figure: Arch Leg 1979

Lithograph, 27.3 × 40.9 image
CGM 541, P5177

MOORE Henry 1898–1986
Reclining Figure: Cave 1979

Lithograph, 30.2 × 40.9 image
CGM 542, P5178

MOORE Henry 1898–1986
Reclining Figure: Distorted 1979

Etching, 22.5 × 28.3 plate
CGM 509, P5180

MOORE Henry 1898–1986
Reclining Figure: Piranesi Background I 1979

Etching and drypoint, 15.9 × 27.9 plate
CGM 510, P5183

MOORE Henry 1898–1986
Reclining Figure: Piranesi Background II 1979

Etching, 22.5 × 28.3 plate
CGM 511, P5184

MOORE Henry 1898–1986
**Reclining Figure: Piranesi
Background III** 1979

Etching, 22.5 × 28.3 plate
CGM 512, P5185

MOORE Henry 1898–1986
Reclining Figure: Pointed 1979

Lithograph, 33 × 41.9 image
CGM 543, P5186

MOORE Henry 1898–1986
Seated Figure 1979

Etching and drypoint, 22.5 × 17.1 plate
CGM 516, P5189

MOORE Henry 1898–1986
**Seated Figure with Architecture
Background** 1979

Etching, 17.5 × 17.1 plate
CGM 517, P5197

MOORE Henry 1898–1986
Seated Woman 1979

Etching, 22.5 × 16.5 plate
CGM 520, P5199

MOORE Henry 1898–1986
Six Sculpture Ideas 1979

Lithograph, 31.7 × 42.5 image
CGM 545, P5203

MOORE Henry 1898–1986
Sleeping Child 1979

Etching, 18.8 × 25.1 plate
CGM 499, P5204

MOORE Henry 1898–1986
The Artist's Hand 1979

A portfolio of two etchings and three
lithographs
Sizes vary
Published by Raymond Spencer
Company Ltd. for the Henry Moore
Foundation, Much Hadham 1980
Edition of 50
P5206–P5210

The Artist's Hand I

Lithograph, 27.7 × 18.4 image
CGM 553, P5206

The Artist's Hand II

Etching, 19 × 25.4 plate
CGM 554, P5207

The Artist's Hand III

Lithograph, 31.7 × 27 image
CGM 555, P5208

P5209

The Artist's Hand IV

Etching, 22.5 × 16.8 plate
CGM 556, P5209

The Artist's Hand V

Lithograph, 26 × 19.4 image
CGM 557, P5210

MOORE Henry 1898–1986
Trees 1979

An album of six etchings
Each sheet 54 × 44.5; image sizes vary
Published by Raymond Spencer
Company Ltd. for the Henry Moore
Foundation, Much Hadham 1980
Edition of 50
P5216–P5221

Trees I: Bole and Creeper

Etching and aquatint, 23.8 × 18.8 plate
CGM 547, P5216

P5217

Trees II: Upright Branches

Etching, drypoint and aquatint
23.2 × 15.9 plate
CGM 548, P5217

Trees III: Knuckled Trunk

Etching, drypoint and aquatint
19 × 25.4 plate
CGM 549, P5218

Trees IV: Tortured Roots

Etching, drypoint and aquatint
24.2 × 18.8 plate
CGM 550, P5219

Trees V: Spreading Branches

Etching and aquatint, 16.8 × 20.6 plate
CGM 551, P5220

Trees VI: Dead Ash

Etching and aquatint, 22.2 × 16.8 plate
CGM 552, P5221

MOORE Henry 1898–1986
Woman Putting on Stocking I 1979

Etching, 25.4 × 19 plate
CGM 521, P5233

MOORE Henry 1898–1986
Reclining Mother and Child I 1979

Etching and drypoint, 22.5 × 28.3 plate
CGM 513, P5855

MOORE Henry 1898–1986
**Reclining Mother and Child I:
Profile** 1979

Etching and drypoint, 22.5 × 28.3 plate
CGM 514, P5856

MOORE Henry 1898–1986
Reclining Mother and Child II
1979

Etching and drypoint, 22.2 × 27.9 plate
CGM 515, P5857

MOORE Henry 1898–1986
Three etchings accompanying
**Sketchbook 1928: The West Wind
Relief** 1979–80, a publication consisting
of a facsimile and explanatory catalogue
on the **West Wind Relief** carving on the
Headquarters building of London
Transport, St. James's, London
Published by Raymond Spencer
Company Ltd. for the Henry Moore
Foundation, Much Hadham 1982
Edition of 410 sketchbooks
P5235–P5237

Reclining Figure 1979

Etching and aquatint, 16.8 × 22.2 plate
CGM 571, P5235

P5236

Idea for Relief Sculpture 1980

Etching and aquatint, 21.9 × 16.8 plate
CGM 572, P5236

Reclining Nude 1980

Etching and aquatint, 22.2 × 29.8 plate
CGM 573, P5237

MOORE Henry 1898–1986
Seated Mother and Child 1979–80

Lithograph, 41.9 × 28.3 image
CGM 570, P5238

MOORE Henry 1898–1986
Seated Figure 1980

Lithograph, 32.1 × 37.2 image
CGM 578, P5056

MOORE Henry 1898–1986
Adam 1980

Lithograph, 26.4 × 33.3 image
CGM 574, P5239

MOORE Henry 1898–1986
Eve 1980

Lithograph, 26.7 × 35.6 image
CGM 575, P5240

MOORE Henry 1898–1986
**Female Figures with Grey
Background** 1980

Lithograph, 22.9 × 44.5 image
CGM 576, P5241

MOORE Henry 1898–1986
Sculptural Ideas 1980

A portfolio of seven etchings
Each sheet 43.2 × 58.1; plate sizes vary
Published by Raymond Spencer
Company Ltd. for the Henry Moore
Foundation, Much Hadham in
association with 2 RC Editrice, Rome
1981
Edition of 50
P5242–P5248

Sculptural Ideas 1

Etching and aquatint, 25.1 × 34.6 plate
CGM 580, P5242

Sculptural Ideas 2

Etching, aquatint and roulette
25.1 × 34.6 plate
CGM 581, P5243

Sculptural Ideas 3

Etching and aquatint, 21.9 × 24.5 plate
CGM 582, P5244

Sculptural Ideas 4

Etching and aquatint, 25.1 × 34.6 plate
CGM 583, P5245

Sculptural Ideas 5

Etching and aquatint, 25.1 × 34.6 plate
CGM 584, P5246

Sculptural Ideas 6

Etching and aquatint, 25.1 × 34.6 plate
CGM 585, P5247

Sculptural Ideas 7

Etching and aquatint, 25.1 × 34.6 plate
CGM 586, P5248

MOORE Henry 1898–1986
Reclining Woman I 1980–81

Lithograph, 52.4 × 59 image
CGM 591, P5249

MOORE Henry 1898–1986
Reclining Woman II 1980–81

Lithograph, 41.9 × 51.4 image
CGM 592, P5250

MOORE Henry 1898–1986
Reclining Woman III 1980–81

Lithograph, 47.7 × 64.8 image
CGM 593, P5251

MOORE Henry 1898–1986
Reclining Woman IV 1980–81

Lithograph, 48.3 × 61.3 image
CGM 594, P5252

MOORE Henry 1898–1986
Reclining Woman on Beach
1980–81

Lithograph, 55.2 × 75.9 image
CGM 595, P5253

P5254

MOORE Henry 1898–1986
Reclining Woman on Sea Shore
1980–81

Lithograph, 44.5 × 61 image
CGM 596, P5254

MOORE Henry 1898–1986
Figures with Sky Background II
1981

Lithograph, 25.7 × 34.6 image
CGM 609, P5141

P5255

MOORE Henry 1898–1986
Elephant's Head I 1981

Lithograph, 27.9 × 23.5 image
CGM 606, P5255

MOORE Henry 1898–1986
Elephant's Head II 1981

Lithograph, 23.2 × 23.2 image
CGM 607, P5256

P5257

MOORE Henry 1898–1986
Figures with Sky Background I
1981

Lithograph, 27 × 27.3 image
CGM 608, P5257

MOORE Henry 1898–1986
Five Ideas for Sculpture 1981

Lithograph, 35.3 × 25.1 image
CGM 610, P5258

MOORE Henry 1898–1986
**Six Reclining Figures with Red
Background** 1981

Lithograph, 21.9 × 24.8 image
CGM 618, P5259

MOORE Henry 1898–1986
Three Sculpture Ideas 1981

Lithograph, 36.8 × 27.7 image
CGM 619, P5260

MOORE Henry 1898–1986
Three Seated Figures 1981

Lithograph, 33 × 28.3 image
CGM 620, P5261

MOORE Henry 1898–1986
Three Sisters 1981

Lithograph, 35.3 × 25.1 image
CGM 621, P5262

MOORE Henry 1898–1986
Ideas for Metal Sculpture I 1981

Lithograph, 22.5 × 24.5 image
CGM 611, P5263

MOORE Henry 1898–1986
Ideas for Metal Sculpture II 1981

Lithograph, 22.5 × 24.5 image
CGM 612, P5264

MOORE Henry 1898–1986
Ideas for Metal Sculpture III 1981

Lithograph, 25.1 × 22.5 image
CGM 613, P5265

MOORE Henry 1898–1986
Ideas for Metal Sculpture IV 1981

Lithograph, 22.2 × 24.5 image
CGM 614, P5266

MOORE Henry 1898–1986
Ideas for Metal Sculpture V 1981

Lithograph, 22.5 × 24.5 image
CGM 615, P5267

MOORE Henry 1898–1986
Ideas for Metal Sculpture VI 1981

Lithograph, 22.5 × 24.5 image
CGM 616, P5268

MOORE Henry 1898–1986
Mary and Martha 1981

Lithograph, 22.5 × 25.1 image
CGM 622, P5269

MOORE Henry 1898–1986
Nativity 1981

Lithograph, 22.5 × 25.1 image
CGM 623, P5270

MOORE Henry 1898–1986
The Attendants 1981

Lithograph, 22.5 × 25.1 image
CGM 625, P5271

MOORE Henry 1898–1986
The Observers 1981

Lithograph, 22.5 × 25.1 image
CGM 626, P5272

MOORE Henry 1898–1986
The Three Marys 1981

Lithograph, 22.5 × 25.1 image
CGM 627, P5273

MOORE Henry 1898–1986
Visitation 1981

Lithograph, 25.1 × 22.5 image
CGM 629, P5274

MOORE Henry 1898–1986
Woman's Head 1981

Lithograph, 22.2 × 25.1 image
CGM 630, P5275

MOORE Henry 1898–1986
Animals in the Zoo 1981–82

An album of 15 etchings
Standard sheet size: portrait 53.3 × 45.7;
landscape 45.7 × 53.3; plate sizes vary
Published by Raymond Spencer
Company Ltd. for the Henry Moore
Foundation, Much Hadham 1983
Edition of 80
P5276–P5290

Elephant's Head 1982

9.8 × 12.4 plate
CGM 631, P5276

Bison 1982

9.8 × 12.4 plate
CGM 632, P5277

Rhinoceros 1982

9.8 × 12.4 plate
CGM 633, P5278

Rhinoceros 1981

21.3 × 27.7 plate
CGM 634, P5279

Dromedary 1981

21.3 × 27.7 plate
CGM 635, P5280

Vultures 1981

21.3 × 27.7 plate
CGM 636, P5281

Elephant 1981

21.3 × 27.7 plate
CGM 637, P5282

Leopard 1981

Etching, aquatint and roulette
25.1 × 19.4 plate
CGM 638, P5283

P5284

Zebra 1981

21.3 × 27.7 plate
CGM 639, P5284

Bison 1981

21.3 × 27.7 plate
CGM 640, P5285

Jaguar 1981

Etching and aquatint
21.3 × 27.7 plate
CGM 641, P5286

Antelope 1982

21.3 × 27.7 plate
CGM 642, P5287

Tiger 1982

19 × 23.8 plate
CGM 643, P5288

Tiger 1982

27.3 × 34.9 plate
CGM 644, P5289

Elephant 1981

27.3 × 35.3 plate
CGM 645, P5290

MOORE Henry 1898–1986
Six Heads: Olympians 1982

Lithograph, 85.7 × 59.3 image
CGM 657, P5057

MOORE Henry 1898–1986
Four Ideas for Sculpture 1982

Lithograph, 23.5 × 30.5 image
CGM 649, P5059

MOORE Henry 1898–1986
Reclining Figure: Bone 1982

Lithograph, 25.1 × 35.3 image
CGM 652, P5060

MOORE Henry 1898–1986
Kneeling Woman 1982

Lithograph, 32.4 × 25.1 image
CGM 650, P5291

MOORE Henry 1898–1986
Reclining Figure: Idea for Metal Sculpture 1982

Lithograph, 23.5 × 30.8 image
CGM 653, P5292

MOORE Henry 1898–1986
Reclining Mother and Child with Blue Background 1982

Lithograph, 54.6 × 75.3 image
CGM 654, P5293

MOORE Henry 1898–1986
Reclining Mother and Child with Grey Background 1982

Lithograph, 54.6 × 75.3 image
CGM 655, P5294

MOORE Henry 1898–1986
Reclining Woman with Yellow Background 1982

Lithograph, 37.2 × 47 image
CGM 656, P5295

MOORE Henry 1898–1986
Mother and Child 1983

An album of 30 etchings
Sizes vary
Published by Raymond Spencer
Company Ltd. for the Henry Moore
Foundation, Much Hadham 1986
Edition of 65
P5663–P5692

Mother and Child I

Etching and aquatint, 31.4 × 24.8 plate;
62 × 52.1 sheet
CGM 671, P5663

Mother and Child II

Etching and aquatint, 16.2 × 22.5 plate;
44 × 52.1 sheet
CGM 672, P5664

Mother and Child III

Etching, aquatint and roulette
22.5 × 17.8 plate; 52.1 × 44 sheet
CGM 673, P5665

Mother and Child IV

Etching, aquatint and roulette
32.1 × 24.8 plate; 62 × 52.1 sheet
CGM 674, P5666

Mother and Child V

Etching, aquatint and roulette
28 × 21.3 plate; 52.1 × 44 sheet
CGM 675, P5667

Mother and Child VI

Etching and aquatint, 23.8 × 18.8 plate;
52.1 × 44 sheet
CGM 676, P5668

Mother and Child VII

Etching, aquatint and roulette
25.1 × 29.8 plate; 44 × 52.1 sheet
CGM 677, P5669

P5670

Mother and Child VIII

Etching and aquatint
35.6 × 25.1 plate; 62 × 52.1 sheet
CGM 678, P5670

Mother and Child IX

Etching, 21.6 × 20.6 plate; 52.1 × 44 sheet
CGM 679, P5671

Mother and Child X

Etching and aquatint, 23.2 × 38.5 plate;
52.1 × 62 sheet
CGM 680, P5672

Mother and Child XI

Etching, aquatint and roulette
34.6 × 26.4 plate; 62 × 52.1 sheet
CGM 681, P5673

Mother and Child XII

Etching, aquatint and roulette
21.3 × 27.3 plate; 44 × 52.1 sheet
CGM 682, P5674

Mother and Child XIII

Etching, aquatint and roulette
32.7 × 25.7 plate; 62 × 52.1 sheet
CGM 683, P5675

Mother and Child XIV

Etching, aquatint and roulette
23.8 × 18.8 plate; 52.1 × 44 sheet
CGM 684, P5676

Mother and Child XV

Etching, aquatint and roulette
21 × 29.5 plate; 44 × 52.1 sheet
CGM 685, P5677

Mother and Child XVI

Etching, aquatint and roulette
34.6 × 36.5 plate; 62 × 52.1 sheet
CGM 686, P5678

Mother and Child XVII

Etching, aquatint and roulette
21 × 20.3 plate; 52.1 × 44 sheet
CGM 687, P5679

Mother and Child XVIII

Etching, aquatint and roulette
22.2 × 16.5 plate; 52.1 × 44 sheet
CGM 688, P5680

Mother and Child XIX

Etching, 29.8 × 41.9 plate; 52.1 × 62 sheet
CGM 689, P5681

Mother and Child XX

Etching and aquatint, 24.1 × 18.1 plate;
52.1 × 44 sheet
CGM 690, P5682

Mother and Child XXI

Etching, aquatint and roulette
34.6 × 24.8 plate; 62 × 52.1 sheet
CGM 691, P5683

Mother and Child XXII

Etching, 22.9 × 18.1 plate; 52.1 × 44 sheet
CGM 692, P5684

Mother and Child XXIII

Etching, aquatint and roulette
26 × 14.3 plate; 52.1 × 44 sheet
CGM 693, P5685

Mother and Child XXIV

Etching, aquatint and drypoint
21 × 29.5 plate; 44 × 52.1 sheet
CGM 694, P5686

Mother and Child XXV

Etching, aquatint, roulette and drypoint
30.5 × 23.2 plate; 62 × 52.1 sheet
CGM 695, P5687

Mother and Child XXVI

Etching, aquatint and roulette
22.9 × 16.2 plate; 52.1 × 44 sheet
CGM 696, P5688

Mother and Child XXVII

Etching, 22.5 × 17.5 plate; 52.1 × 44 sheet
CGM 697, P5689

Mother and Child XXVIII

Etching, aquatint and roulette
35.9 × 27.7 plate; 62 × 52.1 sheet
CGM 698, P5690

Mother and Child XXIX

Etching, aquatint, roulette and drypoint
21.3 × 27.7 plate; 44 × 52.1 sheet
CGM 699, P5691

Mother and Child XXX

Etching, 24.8 × 16.2 plate; 52.1 × 44 sheet
CGM 700, P5692

MOORE Henry 1898–1986
Two Women Seated on Beach 1984

Lithograph, 31.4 × 46.4 image
CGM 719, P5058

MOORE Henry 1898–1986
Ideas for Figures in a Setting 1984

Lithograph, 30.5 × 25.1 image
CGM 714, P5296

MOORE Henry 1898–1986
Two Ideas for Sculpture 1984

Lithograph, 15.9 × 35.3 image
CGM 718, P5297

MOORE Henry 1898–1986
Man and Woman 1984

Lithograph, 27.7 × 21.9 image
CGM 715, P5298

OLLEY Peter B 1942
Cloud Nine 1984

Screenprint, 70 × 59.8 image;
98 × 77.5 sheet
3/20
Purchased from Anderson O'Day
Gallery July 1984
P4897

ORR Chris B 1943
Glimpses of South America II 1974

Etching and aquatint, 14 × 22.5 plate;
16.5 × 27.4 sheet
14/25
Purchased from Merivale Editions
November 1989
P5724

ORR Chris B 1943
Convictions in the Kitchen 1982

Etching, 14 × 36.6 plate; 38.5 × 47.5 sheet
Artist's proof
Purchased from the artist March 1992
P6052

P6053

ORR Chris B 1943
Vegetables go to School 1983

Etching, 22.7 × 34 plate; 38.3 × 57.2 sheet
14/40
Purchased from the artist March 1992
P6053

ORR Chris B 1943
Vegeatable Wars 1983

Etching, 15 × 36.2 plate; 37.6 × 57.5 sheet
12/40
Purchased from the artist March 1992
P6055

ORR Chris B 1943
Albert and the Lion 1987

From **Artists' Choice**, a portfolio of 48
prints by 48 artists, published 1987 by
the Royal College of Art Printmaking
Course
Etching, 30.5 × 30.5 image and sheet
4/48
Purchased from the Royal College of
Art Printmaking Course August 1987
P5554

ORR Chris B 1943
**Have you ever seen Pasta do West
Side Story?** 1987

Etching, 37.8 × 37.2 plate; 59 × 56.5 sheet
16/75
Purchased from the artist March 1992
P6054

ORR Chris B 1943
The Life of W. Blake 1992

A set of eight etchings, with
counterproof and monoprint
Each 58 × 48 image and sheet
Published by the artist 1992
Numbered 1 of an edition of 20
Purchased from the artist November
1992
P6103 – P6110

Title Page

P6103

Blake at the Royal Academy
Schools

P6104

Blake and Socrates

P6105

Sedition

P6106

Blake's Etching Studio

P6107

Blake in the Country

P6108

Tyger

P6109

The Six Foot Serpent

P6110

PACHECO Ana Maria B 1943
Study I 1995

From **Six Artists, The 1994 Royal
College of Art Portfolio of Prints**,
published by the Royal College of Art
Printmaking Course (portfolio
completed 1995)
Drypoint with engraving
38.5 × 60 image; 57.2 × 75.6 sheet
26/50
Purchased from the Royal College of
Art Printmaking Course June 1994
P6312

PAOLOZZI Eduardo B 1924
For Leonardo 1987

From **Artists' Choice**, a portfolio of 48
prints by 48 artists, published 1987 by
the Royal College of Art Printmaking
Course
Engraving, 23 × 22.5 plate;
30.5 × 30.5 sheet
4/48
Purchased from the Royal College of
Art Printmaking Course August 1987
P5553

PAOLOZZI Eduardo B 1924
Les Chants de Maldoror/Ducasse
1992

From **Six Artists, The 1992 Royal
College of Art Portfolio of Prints**,
published by the Royal College of Art
Printmaking Course
Hand coloured etching
39.5 × 56.5 plate; 57.5 × 75.5 sheet
26/50
Purchased from the Royal College of
Art Printmaking Course March 1993
P6192

PLOWMAN Chris B 1952
Odds & Ends 1987

From **Artists' Choice**, a portfolio of 48
prints by 48 artists, published 1987 by
the Royal College of Art Printmaking
Course
Lithograph, 28 × 28.5 image;
30.5 × 30.5 sheet
4/48
Purchased from the Royal College of
Art Printmaking Course August 1987
P5536

PROCKTOR Patrick B 1936
At the Seahouse – A Severed Hand

From **Artists' Choice**, a portfolio of 48
prints by 48 artists, published 1987 by
the Royal College of Art Printmaking
Course
Etching, 22.4 × 22.4 plate;
30.5 × 30.5 sheet
4/48
Purchased from the Royal College of
Art Printmaking Course August 1987
P5559

QUINN Marc B 1964
**Template for my Future Plastic
Surgery** 1992

From **London**, a portfolio of 11 prints
made by 11 artists working in London,
published 1992 by Charles Booth-
Clibborn under his imprint The
Paragon Press
Screenprint with varnish
86 × 68 image and sheet
38/65
Purchased from Karsten Schubert,
London June 1992
P6072

P6198

RAVILIOUS Tirza 1908–1951
The Crocodile 1929

Wood engraving, 16.5 × 12.6 plate;
29.4 × 20.7 sheet
98/500
Purchased from Merivale Editions
December 1993
P6198

RAVILIOUS Tirza 1908–1951
The Dog Show 1929

Wood engraving, 16.5 × 12.6 plate;
29.3 × 20.8 sheet
98/500
Purchased from Merivale Editions
December 1993
P6199

REDFERN June B 1951

Three works, 1986, from **The Scottish
Bestiary**, 20 prints in various media,
various sizes, by seven Scottish artists
illustrating the writings in poetry and
prose of George Mackay Brown
Published 1986 by Charles Booth-
Clibborn under his imprint The
Paragon Press in a book edition of 60
and a portfolio edition of 50
Purchased from The Paragon Press
December 1986
P5454, P5457, P5462

Wolf

Lithograph, 56 × 76 sheet
(image and text)
Book edition: 26/60
P5454

Lion

Lithograph, 56 × 76 sheet
(image and text)
Book edition: 26/60
P5457

Seal

Lithograph and screenprint
56 × 76 sheet (image and text)
Book edition: 26/60
P5462

REEVE Russell 1895–1970
The Elephant Act

School Print 17 from **School Prints**
1946–49, printed at The Baynard Press
Lithograph, 49.5 × 76.1 image and sheet
Purchased from Merivale Editions
December 1993
P6207

REGO Paula B 1935
Young Predators

From **Artists' Choice**, a portfolio of 48
prints by 48 artists, published 1987 by
the Royal College of Art Printmaking
Course
Etching, 24.5 × 25 plate; 30.5 × 30.5 sheet
4/48
Purchased from the Royal College of
Art Printmaking Course August 1987
P5523

REGO Paula B 1935
Girl with a Little Man and Dog
1987

Etching, 25 × 25 plate; 43 × 37.8 sheet
4/50
Purchased from Marlborough Fine Art
May 1988
P5592

REGO Paula B 1935
Girl sitting on a Dog 1987

Etching, 25 × 25.1 plate; 43 × 38 sheet
14/50
Purchased from Marlborough Fine Art
May 1988
P5593

REGO Paula B 1935
Travellers 1987

Etching, 25.2 × 25.2 plate; 41.5 × 37.7 sheet
17/50
Purchased from Marlborough Fine Art
May 1988
P5594

REGO Paula B 1935
Girl, Her Mother and a Dog 1987

Etching, 25.2 × 25.2 plate; 43.7 × 38.5 sheet
18/50
Purchased from Marlborough Fine Art
May 1988
P5595

REGO Paula B 1935
Night Stories 1987

Etching, 25.2 × 25.2 plate; 41.5 × 38.2 sheet
13/50
Purchased from Marlborough Fine Art
May 1988
P5596

REGO Paula B 1935
Four Girls playing with a Dog 1987

Etching, 25 × 25 plate; 42.5 × 37.8 sheet
37/50
Purchased from Marlborough Fine Art
May 1988
P5597

REGO Paula B 1935
Nursery Rhymes 1989

A portfolio of 25 etchings and aquatints
in an edition of 50. Portfolios
numbered 1 to 15 were produced as a
de-luxe boxed version comprising 25
etchings (of which two are hand tinted)
in an edition of 50, plus one untitled
image from an edition of 15.
Each sheet 52 × 38; plate sizes vary
Numbered 7 of an edition of 50;
Published by Marlborough Graphics
1989
Untitled numbered 7 of an edition of 15
Purchased from Marlborough Fine Art
December 1989
P5770, P5772, P5773, P5775–P5787,
P5789–P5795, P5798–P5800

Dance to your daddy

22.2 × 21.5 plate
P5770

Little Miss Muffet

21 × 22.2 plate
P5772

Little Miss Muffet

21 × 22.2 plate (hand tinted)
P5773

Mary, Mary, quite contrary

22.2 × 21.1 plate
P5775

**There was an old woman who
lived in a shoe**

32.1 × 21.1 plate
P5776

Hickety, pickety, my black hen

22.2 × 21.1 plate
P5777

Sing a song of sixpence

21.1 × 22.6 plate
P5778

Sing a song of sixpence

21.1 × 22.5 plate
P5779

Old Mother Goose

32.2 × 21.4 plate
P5780

Jack and Jill went up the hill

32.2 × 21.4 plate
P5781

A frog he would a-wooing go

22.2 × 21.1 plate
P5782

A frog he would a-wooing go

32.2 × 21.4 plate
P5783

The Grand Old Duke of York

32.4 × 21.1 plate
P5784

How many miles to Babylon?

32 × 21.1 plate
P5785

**Old King Cole was a merry old
soul**

21.1 × 22.2 plate
P5786

Polly put the kettle on

21 × 22.2 plate
P5787

**Three blind mice, see how they
run!**

21.1 × 22.4 plate
P5789

Hey diddle diddle

32.4 × 21.1 plate
P5790

Baa, baa, black sheep

32.4 × 21.1 plate
P5791

Ring-a-ring o'roses

21.1 × 22.2 plate
P5792

Goosey, goosey gander

21.1 × 22.2 plate
P5793

**Ride a cock-horse to Banbury
Cross**

32.2 × 21.4 plate (hand tinted)
P5794

Humpty Dumpty sat on a wall

32.2 × 21 plate
P5795

Who killed Cock Robin?

32.2 × 21.4 plate
P5798

P5799

There was a man of double deed

32.2 × 21.4 plate
P5799

Untitled

21 × 22.5 plate
7/15
P5800

REGO Paula B 1935
Little Miss Muffet* 1989

Etching and aquatint, 22.2 × 21.1 plate;
52 × 38 sheet
7/50
Purchased from Marlborough Fine Art
December 1989
P5771

REGO Paula B 1935
Mary, Mary, quite contrary* 1989

Etching and aquatint, 21.1 × 22.5 plate;
52 × 38 sheet
7/50
Purchased from Marlborough Fine Art
December 1989
P5774

REGO Paula B 1935
**Three blind mice, see how they
run!*** 1989

Etching and aquatint, 22.2 × 21.1 plate;
52 × 38 sheet
7/50
Purchased from Marlborough Fine Art
December 1989
P5788

REGO Paula B 1935
Lady Bird, Lady Bird* 1989

Etching and aquatint, 21.1 × 22.5 plate;
52 × 38 sheet
7/50
Purchased from Marlborough Fine Art
December 1989
P5796

REGO Paula B 1935
Who killed Cock Robin?* 1989

Etching and aquatint, 32.2 × 21.4 plate;
52 × 38 sheet
7/50
Purchased from Marlborough Fine Art
December 1989
P5797

*These prints were not included in the
Nursery Rhymes portfolio

REGO Paula B 1935
Embarkation 1992

From **Six Artists, The 1992 Royal
College of Art Portfolio of Prints**,
published by the Royal College of Art
Printmaking Course
Etching and aquatint, 44.5 × 34.5 plate;
76 × 57 sheet
26/50
Purchased from the Royal College of
Art Printmaking Course March 1993
P6189

REGO Paula B 1935
Crow 1994

From **Nine London Birds**, a portfolio of
nine prints by nine artists, published
1994 by the Byam Shaw School of Art
Etching and aquatint, 22.4 × 18.6 plate;
41.3 × 30.5 sheet
26/80
Purchased from the Byam Shaw School
of Art May 1994
P6282

RHODES Zandra B 1940
Head with Scribbled Jewels

From **Artists' Choice**, a portfolio of 48
prints by 48 artists, published 1987 by
the Royal College of Art Printmaking
Course
Lithograph, 30.5 × 30.5 image and sheet
4/48
Purchased from the Royal College of
Art Printmaking Course August 1987
P5518

ROSOMAN Leonard B 1913
**Ship Series: Man blown in the
Wind**

From **Artists' Choice**, a portfolio of 48
prints by 48 artists, published 1987 by
the Royal College of Art Printmaking
Course
Lithograph, 30.5 × 30.5 image and sheet
4/48
Purchased from the Royal College of
Art Printmaking Course August 1987
P5532

ROTHENSTEIN Michael 1908–1993
Timber Felling in Essex

School Print 5 from **School Prints**
1946–49, printed at The Baynard Press
Lithograph, 49.5 × 76 image and sheet
Purchased from Merivale Editions
December 1993
P6201

ROWNTREE Kenneth B 1915
Tractor in a Landscape

School Print 3 from **School Prints**
1946–49, printed at The Baynard Press
Lithograph, 49.8 × 76 image and sheet
Purchased from Merivale Editions
December 1993
P6202

SANDLE Michael B 1936
The Driver 1985

A set of six etchings
Each sheet 42 × 38; plate sizes vary
Published by Bernard Jacobson 1985
Numbered 32 of an edition of 35
Purchased from Bernard Jacobson
Gallery January 1985
P5135 – P5140

The Driver I

30 × 30.2 plate
P5135

P5136

The Driver II

30 × 30.3 plate
P5136

The Driver III

32.3 × 23.7 plate
P5137

The Driver IV

30 × 30.3 plate
P5138

The Driver V

32.4 × 23.6 plate
P5139

The Driver VI

23.7 × 32.7 plate
P5140

P5350

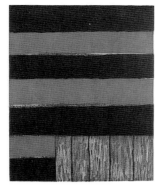

SCULLY Sean B 1945
Cradle 1985

Etching and aquatint, 50.5 × 39.8 plate;
76.1 × 56.5 sheet
6/25
Purchased from Juda Rowan Gallery
March 1986
P5350

SCULLY Sean B 1945
Desire 1985

Etching, 44.9 × 60.5 plate;
56.5 × 76.1 sheet
6/25
Purchased from Juda Rowan Gallery
March 1986
P5351

SCULLY Sean B 1945
Narcissus 1985

Etching and aquatint, 50.7 × 40 plate;
76.1 × 56.5 sheet
6/25
Purchased from Juda Rowan Gallery
March 1986
P5352

SCULLY Sean B 1945
Red Triptych 1985

Etching and aquatint, 44.7 × 60.5 plate;
56.5 × 76.1 sheet
6/25
Purchased from Juda Rowan Gallery
March 1986
P5353

SCULLY Sean B 1945
Union #2 1985

Etching and aquatint, 37.8 × 45.4 plate;
56.5 × 76.2 sheet
6/25
Purchased from Juda Rowan Gallery
March 1986
P5354

SHIOMI Nana B 1956
Blue Venus 1992

From **Six Artists, The 1992 Royal
College of Art Portfolio of Prints**,
published by the Royal College of Art
Printmaking Course
Woodcut, 51 × 35.5 image; 75.5 × 55.5 sheet
26/50
Purchased from the Royal College of
Art Printmaking Course March 1993
P6191

SPEAR Ruskin 1911–1990
Out for the Count 1986

From **Artists' Choice**, a portfolio of 48
prints by 48 artists, published 1987 by
the Royal College of Art Printmaking
Course
Lithograph, 24 × 24 image;
30.5 × 30.5 sheet
4/48
Purchased from the Royal College of
Art Printmaking Course August 1987
P5540

STAHL Andrew B 1954
Night Angel

From **Artists' Choice**, a portfolio of 48
prints by 48 artists, published 1987 by
the Royal College of Art Printmaking
Course
Lithograph, 30.5 × 30.5 image and sheet
4/48
Purchased from the Royal College of
Art Printmaking Course August 1987
P5531

STAHL Andrew B 1954
Figure, Plane, Boat 1988

From **The Culford Press Print Folio
1988**, three prints by three artists,
published by Culford Press, London
Etching and aquatint, 29 × 38 plate;
50 × 55.5 sheet
12/50
Purchased from Culford Press, London
October 1988
P5613

STAINTON Tricia B 1952
Pebbles and Planets

From **Artists' Choice**, a portfolio of 48
prints by 48 artists, published 1987 by
the Royal College of Art Printmaking
Course
Etching, 22.4 × 22.4 plate;
30.5 × 30.5 sheet
4/48
Purchased from the Royal College of
Art Printmaking Course August 1987
P5528

STATON Sarah B 1961
Untitled 1994

From "Other Men's Flowers", text
works by 15 London based artists,
curated by Joshua Compston, and
published 1994 by Charles Booth-
Clibborn under his imprint The
Paragon Press
Letterpress, 47 × 61 sheet
18/100
Purchased from The Paragon Press
November 1994
P6304

STEVENS Norman 1937–1988
Monet's Garden 1987

Screenprint, 61 × 73.7 image;
78.7 × 91.4 sheet
Artist's proof III/XII
Purchased from The Redfern Gallery
December 1992
P6100

STEVENS Norman 1937–1988
Black Walnut Tree 1988

Screenprint, 83.8 × 61 image;
106.7 × 83.8 sheet
Artist's proof x/xv
Purchased from The Redfern Gallery
December 1992
P6101

STEVENS Norman 1937–1988
Fallen Tree, Kensington Gardens
1988

Screenprint, 57.1 × 78.7 image;
78.7 × 99 sheet
Artist's proof x/x
Purchased from The Redfern Gallery
December 1992
P6102

SUTTON Trevor B 1948
**Inside New York – Outside
Larchmont** 1991

A portfolio of six linocuts
Each image 22.8 × 22.7; sheet 35.7 × 35.8
Published by Car Editions, London 1991
Numbered 32 of an edition of 35
Purchased from the artist November
1992
P6121 – P6126

TAYLOR Marcus B 1964
Untitled 1992

From **London**, a portfolio of 11 prints
made by 11 artists working in London,
published 1992 by Charles Booth-
Clibborn under his imprint The
Paragon Press
Screenprint with varnish
86 × 70.5 image and sheet
38/65
Purchased from Karsten Schubert,
London June 1992
P6073

TAYLOR-WOOD Sam B 1967
Untitled 1994

From "Other Men's Flowers", text
works by 15 London based artists,
curated by Joshua Compston, and
published 1994 by Charles Booth-
Clibborn under his imprint The
Paragon Press
Letterpress, 47 × 61 sheet
18/100
Purchased from The Paragon Press,
November 1994
P6305

TILSON Joe B 1928
Masks 1984–85

A set of three prints, various media
Each 115 × 104 image and sheet
Published by Waddington Graphics
1985
Numbered 6 of an edition of 40
Purchased from Waddington Galleries
February 1985
P5002 – P5004

Mask of Poseidon

Etching and aquatint
P5002

Mask of Okeanos

Woodcut, etching and aquatint, with
carborundum
P5003

Mask of Dionysos

Etching and aquatint, with
carborundum
P5004

TILSON Joe B 1928
Liknon 1987

From **Artists' Choice**, a portfolio of 48
prints by 48 artists, published 1987 by
the Royal College of Art Printmaking
Course
Etching and lithograph
30.5 × 30.5 image and sheet
4/48
Purchased from the Royal College of
Art Printmaking Course August 1987
P5548

TILSON Joe B 1928
Metamorphosis of Daphne 1987

Etching, woodcut and carborundum
125 × 109.2 image and sheet
9/35
Purchased from Waddington Galleries
December 1989
P5747

TILSON Joe B 1928
Metamorphosis of Dionysos 1987

Etching, aquatint, woodcut and
carborundum, 125 × 101.6 image and
sheet
9/35
Purchased from Waddington Galleries
December 1989
P5748

TILSON Joe B 1928
Signatures 1987–88

A portfolio of six prints
Various media, various sizes
Published by Waddington Graphics
1988
Numbered 12 of an edition of 40
Purchased from Waddington Galleries
December 1989
P5750 – P5755

Signatures and Correspondences

Etching, aquatint and carborundum,
with gold leaf and white gold leaf
56 × 79 image and sheet
P5750

Star Signatures

Etching and aquatint, with white gold
leaf, 57.5 × 39 image and sheet
P5751

P5752

Sun Signatures

Etching, aquatint and carborundum,
with gold leaf, 57.5 × 39 image and sheet
P5752

Moon Signatures

Etching, aquatint and photo-engraving,
with white gold leaf, 57.5 × 39 image and
sheet
P5753

The Doctrine of Signatures

Etching, aquatint and carborundum,
with white gold leaf
56 × 79 image and sheet
P5754

Signatures of Dionysos

Carborundum, etching and aquatint,
with gold leaf, 56 × 79 image and sheet
P5755

TILSON Joe B 1928
Grania 1994
From the **Crete series 1994**

From **Six Artists, The 1994 Royal
College of Art Portfolio of Prints**,
published by the Royal College of Art
Printmaking Course (portfolio
completed 1995)
Two sheet screenprint and lithograph,
with brass eyelets and string
75.5 × 55 image and top sheet;
78.8 × 57.2 image and underlying sheet
26/50
Purchased from the Royal College of
Art Printmaking Course June 1994
P6313

TINDLE David B 1932
Four Seasons

From **Artists' Choice**, a portfolio of 48
prints by 48 artists, published 1987 by
the Royal College of Art Printmaking
Course
Etching, 23.5 × 24 plate; 30.5 × 30.5 sheet
4/48
Purchased from the Royal College of
Art Printmaking Course August 1987
P5560

P6205

TREVELYAN Julian 1910–1988
Harbour 1946

School Print 9 from **School Prints**
1946–49, printed at The Baynard Press
Lithograph, 49.5 × 76.4 image and sheet
Purchased from Merivale Editions
December 1993
P6205

TREVELYAN Julian 1910–1988
Construction

From **Artists' Choice**, a portfolio of 48
prints by 48 artists, published 1987 by
the Royal College of Art Printmaking
Course
Etching, 15 × 19.5 plate; 30.5 × 30.5 sheet
4/48
Purchased from the Royal College of
Art Printmaking Course August 1987
P5529

TURK Gavin B 1967
**GAVIN TURK RIGHT HAND
AND FOREARM** 1992

From **London**, a portfolio of 11 prints
made by 11 artists working in London,
published 1992 by Charles Booth-
Clibborn under his imprint The
Paragon Press
Screenprint with varnish
86 × 68 image and sheet
38/65
Purchased from Karsten Schubert,
London June 1992
P6074

TURK Gavin B 1967
Untitled 1994

From "Other Men's Flowers", text
works by 15 London based artists,
curated by Joshua Compston, and
published 1994 by Charles Booth-
Clibborn under his imprint The
Paragon Press
Screenprint, 47 × 61 sheet
18/100
Purchased from The Paragon Press
November 1994
P6306

VAUGHAN Michael B 1938
Death and the Maiden 1987

From **Artists' Choice**, a portfolio of 48
prints by 48 artists, published 1987 by
the Royal College of Art Printmaking
Course
Etching, 15.3 × 15.8 plate; 30.5 × 30.5 sheet
4/48
Purchased from the Royal College of
Art Printmaking Course August 1987
P5561

Visual Aid for Band Aid Print 1985

(104 British artists contributed to the
creation of this print)
Screenprint, 120 × 92 image and sheet
49/500
Purchased from Thumb Gallery
December 1985
P5334

VOSPER Clive B 1947
Reflections from both sides 1980

Etching, 35 × 49.2 plate; 50 × 65 sheet
3/5
Purchased from the artist June 1984
P4890

VOSPER Clive B 1947
**Ripples under the over-hanging
Tree** 1981

Etching, 44.5 × 32.5 plate; 66 × 50.3 sheet
8/8
Purchased from the artist June 1984
P4884

VOSPER Clive B 1947
Winter Reflections at the Pells 1981

Etching, 45 × 33 plate; 66 × 50.2 sheet
4/10
Purchased from the artist June 1984
P4888

VOSPER Clive B 1947
Winter Reflections at the Pells II
1981

Etching, 45 × 33 plate; 66 × 50.2 sheet
5/7
Purchased from the artist June 1984
P4889

VOSPER Clive B 1947
The Eyecatcher 1982

Etching, 34.2 × 43.8 plate;
50 × 65.5 sheet
5/15
Purchased from the artist June 1984
P4885

VOSPER Clive B 1947
**'Borrowed' Landscape,
Hestercombe** 1983

Etching, 36.7 × 46.5 plate;
50.3 × 66 sheet
7/15
Purchased from the artist June 1984
P4886

VOSPER Clive B 1947
The Doric Temple, Petworth 1984

Etching, 44 × 35 plate; 66 × 50.2 sheet
5/30
Purchased from the artist June 1984
P4887

WEIGHT Carel B 1908
A Walker from the Past

From **Artists' Choice**, a portfolio of 48
prints by 48 artists, published 1987 by
the Royal College of Art Printmaking
Course
Lithograph, 30.5 × 30.5 image and sheet
4/48
Purchased from the Royal College of
Art Printmaking Course August 1987
P5544

WENTWORTH Richard B 1947
Red Eight 1987

From **Artists' Choice**, a portfolio of 48
prints by 48 artists, published 1987 by
the Royal College of Art Printmaking
Course
Lithograph, 30.5 × 30.5 image and sheet
4/48
Purchased from the Royal College of
Art Printmaking Course August 1987
P5521

WENTWORTH Richard B 1947
Half a Mo 1993

Stainless steel measuring jug, steel
measuring tape and rivets
Height 17, diameter 45.5
14/30
Purchased from Serpentine Gallery
November 1993
P6208

WHITEFORD Kate B 1952
Sitelines 1989

A set of four screenprints
Each image 26 × 20; sheet 51 × 42
Published by Frith Street Gallery 1989
Numbered 22 of an edition of 35
Purchased from Frith Street Gallery
November 1989
P5705 – P5708 (P5706 colour plate 44)

WHITEFORD Kate B 1952
Double Chevron and Spiral 1989

From **King's Fund Prints**, a set of six
prints chosen by Richard Cork,
published 1989 by The King's Fund in
an edition of 250
Screenprint, 122.5 × 96.8 image;
144.4 × 117.4 sheet
226/250
Purchased from the artist January 1990
P5757

WHITEREAD Rachel B 1963
Mausoleum under Construction
(after a photograph by Camilo José
Vergara) 1992

From **London**, a portfolio of 11 prints
made by 11 artists working in London,
published 1992 by Charles Booth-
Clibborn under his imprint The
Paragon Press
Screenprint, 55.6 × 79 image;
71 × 88 sheet
38/65
Purchased from Karsten Schubert,
London June 1992
P6075

WIGRAM Max B 1966
Untitled 1994

From **"Other Men's Flowers"**, text
works by 15 London based artists,
curated by Joshua Compston, and
published 1994 by Charles Booth-
Clibborn under his imprint The
Paragon Press
Screenprint and letterpress
47 × 61 sheet
18/100
Purchased from The Paragon Press
November 1994
P6307 (colour plate 45)

WILKINSON Donald B 1937
Storm over Derwentwater 1975

A series of six etchings and aquatints,
plus frontispiece
Each plate 35.5 × 42; sheet 73 × 57.5
Published by the artist 1975 in an
edition of 75
Artist's proofs
Purchased from the artist November
1984
P4974 – P4980

**Storm over Derwentwater
(Frontispiece)**

21 × 26 plate
P4974

Storm over Derwentwater I

P4975

Storm over Derwentwater II

P4976

Storm over Derwentwater III

P4977

Storm over Derwentwater IV

P4978

Storm over Derwentwater V

P4979

Storm over Derwentwater VI

P4980

WILKINSON Donald B 1937
Iron Crag 1976

Etching and aquatint (vertical triptych)
36 × 46.5 top plate; 37.5 × 46.5 centre
plate; 37.5 × 46.5 bottom plate
111 × 46.5 overall image;
131 × 70 overall sheet
Artist's proof
Purchased from the artist November
1984
P4966

WILKINSON Donald B 1937
A Winter Landscape 1976

Etching and aquatint, 34.5 × 44 plate;
56 × 68.5 sheet
Artist's proof
Purchased from the artist November
1984
P4968

WILKINSON Donald B 1937
The Lake I 1976

Etching and aquatint
Part one of a three part work
49 × 48 plate; 72 × 56 sheet
30/100
Purchased from the artist November
1984
P4971

WILKINSON Donald B 1937
The Lake II 1976

Etching and aquatint
Part two of a three part work
49.5 × 48 plate; 72 × 56 sheet
30/100
Purchased from the artist November
1984
P4972

WILKINSON Donald B 1937
The Lake III 1976

Etching and aquatint
Part three of a three part work
49.5 × 48 plate; 72 × 56 sheet
30/100
Purchased from the artist November
1984
P4973

WILKINSON Donald B 1937
**At the Meeting of the
Water/February** 1978

Etching and aquatint, with embossing
50 × 37.5 plate; 71 × 55.8 sheet
Artist's proof
Purchased from the artist November
1984
P4969

WILKINSON Donald B 1937
Below Derwent Folds 1980

Etching and aquatint (triptych)
49 × 38.5 left plate; 49 × 39 centre plate;
49 × 38.5 right plate
49 × 116 overall image;
69.5 × 139 overall sheet
68/75
Purchased from Anderson O'Day
Gallery June 1984
P4882

WILKINSON Donald B 1937
**Winter Light/Above
Derwentwater** 1980

Etching and aquatint, 38.5 × 47 plate;
57 × 69.5 sheet
Artist's proof
Purchased from the artist November
1984
P4964

P4965

WILKINSON Donald B 1937
**"The Moon stood naked in the
heavens" – Wordsworth – Prelude**
1981

Etching and aquatint (triptych)
48 × 38.5 left plate; 48 × 30 centre plate;
48 × 38.5 right plate
21.5 × 15 text plate below each image
71 × 107 overall image;
80 × 126 overall sheet
Artist's proof
Purchased from the artist November 1984
P4965

WILKINSON Donald B 1937
After Rain Below Carrock/January
1982

Etching and aquatint (diptych)
50 × 41.5 each plate
50 × 83 overall image;
71 × 103 overall sheet
1/80
Purchased from Thumb Gallery April
1984
P4874

WILKINSON Donald B 1937
Fellside in Winter Sunlight 1982

Etching and aquatint (diptych)
39.5 × 48 each plate
39.5 × 96 overall image;
56 × 118 overall sheet
Artist's proof
Purchased from the artist November
1984
P4963

WILKINSON Donald B 1937
**Towards Lonscale and
Saddleback/Snow Clouds** 1984

Etching and aquatint (diptych)
51.5 × 39 each plate
51.5 × 78 overall image;
71 × 99 overall sheet
51/80
Purchased from Thumb Gallery April
1984
P4873

WILKINSON Donald B 1937
**Sunlight and Rain moving across
Nab Scar/Winter Morning** 1984

Etching and aquatint (diptych)
39.5 × 48.5 left plate; 39.5 × 49 right plate
39.5 × 97.5 overall image;
58.5 × 121 overall sheet
23/80
Purchased from Thumb Gallery April
1984
P4875

WILKINSON Donald B 1937
Langstrath Valley/Storm Clearing
1984

Etching and aquatint (diptych)
49 × 40 each plate
49 × 80 overall image;
71 × 102 overall sheet
Artist's proof
Purchased from the artist November
1984
P4967

P4970

WILKINSON Donald B 1937
Frozen Lake/February Morning
1984

Etching and aquatint, 37.5 × 45 plate;
58.5 × 55 sheet
Artist's proof
Purchased from the artist November
1984
P4970

WISZNIEWSKI Adrian B 1958
Three works, 1986, from both the book
and portfolio editions of **The Scottish
Bestiary**, 20 prints in various media,
various sizes, by seven Scottish artists
illustrating the writings in poetry and
prose of George Mackay Brown
Published by Charles Booth-Clibborn
under his imprint The Paragon Press, in
a book edition of 60 and a portfolio
edition of 50
Book edition works purchased from
The Paragon Press December 1986
P5452, P5459, P5464
Portfolio edition works purchased from
The Paragon Press April 1987
P5489, P5490, P5491

Raven

Screenprint, 56 × 76 sheet (image and text)
Book edition: 26/60
P5452

Dragon

Lithograph, 56 × 76 sheet (image and text)
Book edition: 26/60
P5459

Unicorn

Etching, 56 × 76 sheet (image and text)
Book edition: 26/60
P5464

Raven

Screenprint, 53.5 × 35.5 image;
76 × 56.5 sheet
Portfolio edition: 15/50
P5489

Unicorn

Etching, 51.5 × 33.7 plate; 76 × 56.5 sheet
Portfolio edition: 15/50
P5490

Dragon

Lithograph, 53.2 × 34.2 image;
76 × 56.5 sheet
Portfolio edition: 15/50
P5491

WISZNIEWSKI Adrian B 1958
The Sculptor's Nightmare 1986

Etching and aquatint, 60.5 × 91 plate;
74 × 104 sheet
33/70
Purchased from Glasgow Print Studio
November 1989
P5736

P5806

WISZNIEWSKI Adrian B 1958
Poet 1986

Screenprint, 94.5 × 129.5 image;
106.5 × 139.5 sheet
47/50
Purchased from Nigel Greenwood
Gallery April 1990
P5806

WISZNIEWSKI Adrian B 1958
Chez Nous 1987

Woodcut, four sheets joined
238 × 178 overall image;
243 × 183 overall sheet
13/25
Purchased from Glasgow Print Studio
November 1989
P5737

WISZNIEWSKI Adrian B 1958
For Max 1988

A book of 25 colour linocuts, plus
frontispiece
Each image 23.3 × 19; sheet 26.6 × 21.5
Published by Charles Booth-Clibborn
under his imprint The Paragon Press
1988
Numbered 17 of an edition of 100
Purchased from The Paragon Press
March 1988
P5586 A–Y (P5586K colour plate 46)

WISZNIEWSKI Adrian B 1958
Fishermen 1989

Screenprint and lithograph
63 × 46.5 image; 76 × 56 sheet
11/20
Purchased from Nigel Greenwood
Gallery April 1990
P5807

WOOD Craig B 1960
**Safeway Gel Air Freshener, Alpine
Garden (detail)** 1992

From **London**, a portfolio of 11 prints
made by 11 artists working in London,
published 1992 by Charles Booth-
Clibborn under his imprint The
Paragon Press
Screenprint with mould cut sections
and varnish, 66 × 86 sheet
38/65
Purchased from Karsten Schubert,
London June 1992
P6076 (colour plate 47)

35 CRAIGIE AITCHISON
Wayney going to Heaven 1989

P5744

36 PATRICK CAULFIELD
**Ah! this Life is so
everyday** 1973
P5031

37 TERRY FROST
Lemon Glow 1991
P6193

38 PETER HOWSON
Stag 1986
P5480

39 BARBARA JONES
Fairground
from **School Prints**
1946–49
P6200

40 BRUCE MCLEAN
Hot Slick 1989
P5756

41 TIM MARA
Coal and Diamonds 1985
P6315

42 HENRY MOORE
Petals 1974
P5103

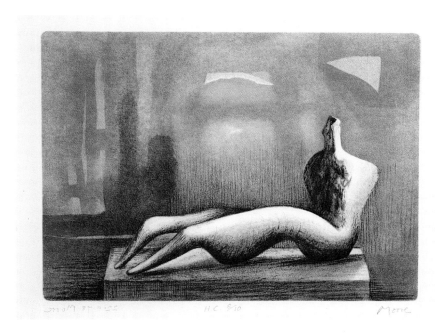

43 HENRY MOORE
Reclining Figure: Sunset 1978
P5187

44 KATE WHITEFORD
Sitelines 1989
P5706

CHARNEL

45 MAX WIGRAM
Untitled 1994
P6307

46 ADRIAN WISZNIEWSKI
For Max 1988
P5586K

47 CRAIG WOOD
**Safeway Gel Air Freshener,
Alpine Garden (detail)** 1992
P6076

PART IV : **Photography**

In 1981, following an internal review, Fine Arts Department (re-named Visual Arts Department in 1988) assumed responsibility for the subject area of photography. Previously, the British Council's General Exhibitions Department had initiated touring shows of reportage and documentary photography, whereas Fine Arts Department had concentrated on showing and acquiring work by artists such as Hamish Fulton and Richard Long, whose practice incorporates photography. In 1982 an Exhibition Officer was appointed to develop a coherent policy for the promotion of photography as an independent medium. The policy aims were to demonstrate the versatility of the medium and its significance within contemporary visual art, as well as to stimulate an awareness and understanding overseas of Britain's contribution to the development of photography over the last 150 years. Since the implementation of this policy, fifteen exhibitions drawn from new works purchased for the British Council Collection have been created and toured.

Entries are arranged by artist in alphabetical order. Where an artist has more than one work in the Collection, the works are given in chronological order. Works of the same year are listed in British Council Collection accession number sequence, unless the actual day or month of completion is known.

1. Name of artist and date of birth (and death).

2. Title of work. Please note that many of the photographs listed are from an identifiable sequence, series, publication or exhibition. In such cases, the generic title precedes the individual titles of the works. Details of specifically related monographs are given as footnotes.

3. Date of work. The dates which follow generic titles refer to the year or period during which the works comprising the entire sequence, series, publication or exhibition were executed. A single date followed by a hyphen indicates that at the time of writing the artist considers this sequence/series on-going. The dates of individual works (when different from the generic dates) follow individual titles.

4. Medium.

5. Dimensions are given in centimetres, height preceding width. Unless otherwise stated, the dimensions are of the original surface, without frame.

6. Edition number (where appropriate).

7. Source and date of acquisition.

8. British Council Collection accession number.

There is one illustration to accompany each sequence, series, publication or exhibition, and one illustration per individual entry.

In this section of the catalogue artists' signatures and inscriptions are not noted.

ANDREWS Lea B 1958
From **Public Sculpture, Private Land** 1989

Two Cibachrome prints
Purchased from the artist April 1990
P5808 (illustrated), P5809

Maquette for 'Young Tom and Dobbin discover Sonning Common'

122.5 × 170.2
P5808

Maquette for 'War Memorial for Sonning Common'

122.5 × 181
P5809

ARNATT Keith B 1930
From **Forest of Dean** 1986

Four untitled silver gelatin prints
Each 26 × 33
Purchased from the artist January 1987
P5475–P5478 (P5476 illustrated)

ARNATT Keith B 1930
From **The Open Door** 1986

Nine untitled C-type colour prints (one frame); and two calotype facsimiles (one frame) of **The Open Door** by W H Fox Talbot
Purchased from the artist January 1987
C-type colour prints: each 18 × 18
P5487A–I

Calotype facsimiles: 15.8 × 18 left calotype; 13.5 × 18.4 right calotype
P5488A, P5488B

ARNATT Keith B 1930
From **Objects from a Rubbish Tip** 1989 –

Eight untitled C-type colour prints 1989
Each 94.3 × 113.2
Purchased from Zelda Cheatle Gallery November 1989
P5697–P5704 (P5701 illustrated)
(P5697 colour plate 48)

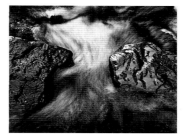

BLAKEMORE John[1] B 1936
From **All Flows** 1974–75

Lynch Clough, Derbyshire 1975

Silver gelatin selenium toned print
50 × 60
Purchased from Zelda Cheatle Gallery December 1992
P6141

BLAKEMORE John B 1936
From **Sound of the Sea** 1975–77

Two silver gelatin selenium toned prints: each 50 × 60
Purchased from Zelda Cheatle Gallery December 1992
P6142 (illustrated), P6143

Rocks and Tide, Friog, Wales 1977

P6142

Rocks and Tide, Friog, Wales 1977

P6143

BLAKEMORE John B 1936
From **Lila** 1977–79

Three silver gelatin selenium toned prints: each 40 × 50
Purchased from Zelda Cheatle Gallery December 1992
P6144-P6146 (P6146 illustrated)

Ambergate, Derbyshire 1978

P6144

Lathkill Dale, Derbyshire 1978

P6145

Shirley, Derbyshire 1978

P6146

BLAKEMORE John B 1936
From **Windseries II** 1981

Two silver gelatin selenium toned prints: each 50 × 60
Purchased from Zelda Cheatle Gallery December 1992
P6147 (illustrated), P6148

Ambergate, Derbyshire

P6147

Ambergate, Derbyshire

P6148

BLAKEMORE John B 1936
From **Thistle** 1980–82

Two silver gelatin selenium toned prints
Purchased from Zelda Cheatle Gallery December 1992
P6149 (illustrated), P6150

Thistle 1982

50 × 40
P6149

Thistle 1982

40 × 50
P6150

BLAKEMORE John B 1936
From **Tulipomania** 1983–94

Seven silver gelatin selenium toned prints
Purchased from Zelda Cheatle Gallery December 1992
P6151–P6157 (P6153 illustrated)

Tulips 1988

50 × 60
P6151

Tulips 1990

50 × 60
P6152

Tulips 1991

60 × 50
P6153

Tulip, The Generations No. 1 1991

50 × 60
P6154

Tulip, The Generations No. 4 1991

50 × 60
P6155

Tulip, Mutations No. 1 1991

50 × 60
P6156

Tulip, Mutations No. 7 1992

60 × 50
P6157

BLAKEMORE John B 1936
From **Chimerical Landscapes** 1990

Chimerical Landscapes 1

Silver gelatin selenium toned print
40 × 50
Purchased from Zelda Cheatle Gallery December 1992
P6160

BLAKEMORE John B 1936
From **The Garden – Fragments of a History** 1991–92

Two works: each 50 × 60
Purchased from Zelda Cheatle Gallery December 1992
P6158, P6159 (P6159 illustrated)

Amergen – The Garden in Winter 1991

Silver gelatin selenium and gold toned print
P6158

The Garden – Fragments of a History 3 1991

Silver gelatin selenium toned print
P6159

BRANDT Bill[2] 1904–1983
In 1972 60 photographs were printed under the artist's supervision to a standard portrait size of 60 × 51. They were purchased from him in December of the same year, and formed the circulating exhibition *Bill Brandt Photographs*, which toured 1973–1994 (P4731 illustrated)

See Appendix for individual entries

CHADWICK Helen B 1953
From **Meat Abstract #1–8** 1989

Four colour Polaroid prints
Each 70 × 53.5
Edition 3/4
Purchased from the artist January 1990
P5760–P5763 (P5760 illustrated)

Meat Abstract #1

P5760

Meat Abstract #3

P5761

Meat Abstract #4

P5762

Meat Abstract #8

P5763

CHAPLIN Bob B 1947
Hardberry Hill up to the Weather Beds, The Moors, County Durham 1978

Photo-collage, incorporating one 'found' commercial aerial photograph, six hand tinted prints, and hand lettering (one frame)
102.5 × 70.7 overall size (image and text)
Purchased from the artist September 1984
P4913

CHAPLIN Bob B 1947
William's Gill, North Riding 1978

Photo-collage, incorporating three 'found' commercial aerial photographs, one hand tinted print, and hand lettering (one frame)
103 × 73.5 overall size (image and text)
Purchased from the artist September 1984
P4914

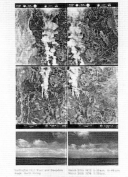

CHAPLIN Bob B 1947
Lartington High Moor and Deepdale Beck, North Riding 1978

Photo-collage, incorporating four 'found' commercial aerial photographs, two hand tinted prints, and hand lettering (one frame)
103 × 71 overall size (image and text)
Purchased from the artist September 1984
P4915

CHAPLIN Bob B 1947
Rackwick Bay: Hoy Orkney 1979

Six C-type colour prints (one frame)
44.5 × 77 overall size
One of an edition of ten
Purchased from the artist September 1984
P4916

CHAPLIN Bob B 1947
Chanctonbury (South Downs), Heaven's Gate, Jullieberry (North Downs) 1982

Four C-type colour prints, with pencil and hand lettering (one frame)
72 × 62 overall size (image and text)
Purchased from Calvert Intergraphic Ltd., London September 1984
P4928

CHAPLIN Bob B 1947
Jullieberry (North Downs), Heaven's Gate, Chanctonbury (South Downs) 1982

Two C-type colour prints, with pencil and hand lettering (one frame)
72 × 62 overall size (image and text)
Purchased from Calvert Intergraphic Ltd., London September 1984
P4929

CHAPLIN Bob B 1947
Scafell Pikes, Catchedicam, Coniston Old Man, Swirl How 1984

Four silver prints, with screenprinted text and letterpress (one frame)
132 × 50.8 overall size (image and text)
Purchased from Calvert Intergraphic Ltd., London September 1984
P4927

COLLINS Hannah B 1956
Untitled 1990

Silver gelatin print, mounted on cotton
143.8 × 189.2
Purchased from Maureen Paley/Interim Art October 1990
P5828

COLLINS Hannah B 1956
Untitled 1990

Silver gelatin print, mounted on cotton
198.6 × 129.1
Purchased from Maureen Paley/Interim Art October 1990
P5829

COLLINS Hannah B 1956
Eggs for Bread 1991

Silver gelatin print, in two parts, laid on aluminium, 158 × 135 overall size
Purchased from the artist June 1992
P6128

COLVIN Calum[3] B 1961
The Death of Venus 1986

Cibachrome print, 50.8 × 40.6
Purchased from the artist July 1987
P5503

COLVIN Calum B 1961
Explorer I 1986

Cibachrome print, 50.8 × 40.6
Purchased from the artist July 1987
P5504

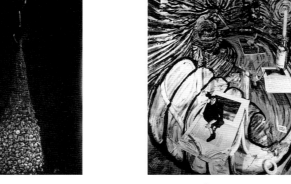

COLVIN Calum B 1961
Deaf Man's Villa 1989

Cibachrome prints (triptych: each print framed separately)
124.5 × 97.4 left print; 153.8 × 122 centre print; 124.5 × 97.4 right print
One of an edition of ten
Purchased from Salama-Caro Gallery March 1990
P5827 (colour plate 49)

COLVIN Calum B 1961
From **The Seven Deadly Sins and the Four Last Things** 1993
Avarice

Cibachrome print, 82 × 102
Purchased from Portfolio Gallery, Edinburgh April 1994
P6272

Cutting Lawrence B 1939
From **Racing Seen** 1964 –

Six silver prints: each 38 × 30.5
Purchased from the artist November 1986
P5440–P5445 (P5440 illustrated)

Flower Festival in Parish Church, Middleham, North Yorkshire 1974

P5440

Fish and Chip Van on Course, Ballinrobe, Ireland 1983

P5445

Abandoned Bookie's Bag on Free Course, Hamilton Park, Glasgow 1984

P5441

Grandstand, Lanark, Scotland 1984

P5443

Alice Hawthorn Pub Sign on Vegetable Stall, York 1985

P5442

Alice Hawthorn Pub Sign on Wasteland outside Course, York 1985

P5444

Davies John[4] B 1949
From **A Green & Pleasant Land** 1981–86

Three silver bromide prints
Each 50 × 60
Purchased from the artist February 1992; March 1993
P6064, P6170, P6171 (P6170 illustrated)

'Durham Ox' Public House, Sheffield, Yorkshire 1981

Purchased from the artist February 1992
P6064

Stockport with descending Airliner, Stockport, Cheshire 1985

Purchased from the artist March 1993
P6171

Dismantled Railway Bridge, Accrington, Lancashire 1986

Purchased from the artist March 1993
P6170

Fox Anna B 1961
From **Friendly Fire (A Study of Weekend Wargames in Britain)** 1990–94

Two untitled C-type colour prints, with text: each 65 × 75.5 (framed)
Purchased from the artist April 1993
P6168 (illustrated), P6169

Untitled

['I didn't like the sound of this as a business when I first started it. I'm a vegetarian and a pacifist you know.' PAINTBALL MANAGER]
P6168

Untitled

['A real adrenalin-booster . . . Vietcong village, genuine World War II jail block, tunnels and trenches.' GAME ADVERTISEMENT]
P6169

Fraser Peter B 1953
From **Everyday Icons** 1985–86

Four C-type colour prints
Each 40.3 × 50.5
Purchased from The Photographers' Gallery July 1986
P5401, P5402, P5403, P5406 (P5406 illustrated)

Chew Stoke No. 1 1985

P5401

Pilton near Shepton Mallet 1985

P5402

Easton near Wells 1985

P5403

Chew Stoke No. 2 1985

P5406

Davies John B 1949
From **Cross Currents** 1982–92
Canadian Memorial, Vimy 1989

Silver bromide print, 50.8 × 61
Purchased from the artist April 1993
P6180

Fraser Peter[5] B 1953

From **The Valleys Project** 1985

Two C-type colour prints
Each 40.3 × 50.5
Purchased from The Photographers' Gallery July 1986
P5404, P5405 (P5405 illustrated)

Trealaw near Porth

P5404

Pontypridd No. 1

P5405

Germain Julian[6] B 1962
From **Steelworks** 1986–90

Two C-type colour prints (in artist-constructed frames)
Purchased from the artist March 1993
P6166, P6167 (P6167 illustrated)

283 Hectares (423 Football Pitches)

61.3 × 74.2; framed 67.5 × 80.4
P 6166

Consett Bus Station built with Italian Steel

61.2 × 74.8; framed 67.5 × 81
P6167

Julian Germain's works are shown in conjunction with two untitled black and white press photographs by Tommy Harris (a local photographer, working for newspapers in Consett 1949–70)
Each 25.2 × 23
Purchased from the photographer (via Julian Germain) March 1993
P6166A, P6167A,
(P6167A illustrated)

GOLDSWORTHY Andy B 1956
Sycamore leaf, found on cow dung – peeled off and placed on dry light leaves
North Yorkshire March 1980
Sycamore leaf, bleached with age – placed on roughed up damp leaves
West Yorkshire 30 January 1981
Two Cibachrome prints (in one artist-constructed frame)
Each 23.7 × 15.7; framed 44.5 × 60.5
One of an edition of five
Purchased from Common Ground December 1985
P5336

GOLDSWORTHY Andy B 1956
Balanced Rocks
Morecambe Bay, Lancashire May 1978
Cibachrome print (in an artist-constructed frame)
35 × 49; framed 60 × 74
One of an edition of five
Purchased from Common Ground December 1985
P5339

GOLDSWORTHY Andy B 1956
Poppy petals | early morning, before breeze strengthened | each petal licked underneath and pressed to another | to make a line about seven feet long
Haarlemmerhout, Holland 27 August 1984
Four Cibachrome prints (displayed in two artist-constructed frames)
Primary frame: three Cibachrome prints, 48.2 × 31.4; 48.9 × 31.7; 47.6 × 30.8; joined 113.5 × 43.5; framed 149 × 64
Secondary frame: single Cibachrome print, 39 × 26; framed 60.2 × 51
One of an edition of three
Purchased from Common Ground December 1985
P5335

GOLDSWORTHY Andy B 1956
Sycamore stalks in grass | raining
Helbeck, Cumbria November 1984
Two Cibachrome prints (in one artist-constructed frame)
38.1 × 25.4 left print; 25.4 × 38.1 right print; 58.4 × 92.7 framed
One of an edition of five
Purchased from Common Ground December 1985
P5340

GOLDSWORTHY Andy B 1956
Snowball in trees
Low Bentham, Lancashire February 1980
Cibachrome print (in an artist-constructed frame)
31.5 × 49; framed 60 × 74
One of an edition of five
Purchased from Common Ground December 1985
P5334A

GOLDSWORTHY Andy B 1956
Shallow pond | frozen over with thin ice | broke and removed a section | used pieces with pointed ends, held upright in muddy pond bottom | calm
Helbeck, Cumbria 23 January 1983

Two Cibachrome prints (in one artist-constructed frame)
48.5 × 31.5 left print; 31.5 × 48.5 right print; 64 × 107 framed
One of an edition of five
Purchased from Common Ground December 1985
P5337

GOLDSWORTHY Andy B 1956
Leaf patches | edges made by finding leaves the same size | tearing one in two | spitting underneath and pressing flat on to one another
Swindale Beck Wood, Cumbria Red Patch (Cherry) 4 November 1984
Two Cibachrome prints (in one artist-constructed frame)
38 × 25.5 left print; 38 × 38.5 right print; 60 × 93.5 framed
One of an edition of five
Purchased from Common Ground December 1985
P5338

GRAHAM Paul[7] B 1956
From **Troubled Land The Social Landscape of Northern Ireland** 1984–86

Six colour carbon prints
At the request of the artist, sizes are not given
Purchased from the artist June 1986
P5385–P5390 (P5385 illustrated)

Republican coloured Kerbstones, Crumlin Road, Belfast 1984

P5388

Roundabout, Andersonstown, Belfast 1984

P5389

Graffiti on Roadsign near Toome 1984

P5390

Union Jack Flag in Tree, County Tyrone 1985

P5385

Fading Political Posters, County Tyrone 1985

P5386

Graffiti on Phonebox, Belfast 1985

P5387

HEAD Tim B 1946
Fall Out 1985

Cibachrome print, 123.5 × 93.5
One of an edition of three
Purchased from Nicola Jacobs Gallery October 1990
P5832

HURN David B 1934
From **Wales Black and White** 1971–73

38 silver prints
Printed to a standard size: portrait 29.5 × 20; landscape 20 × 29.5
Purchased from the artist October 1975
These works formed the circulating exhibition *Wales Black and White: Photographs by David Hurn*, which toured 1976–1985
(P6251 illustrated)
See Appendix for individual entries

KIPPIN John B 1950
(HIDDEN) National Park, Northumberland 1991

C-type colour print, with screenprinted text, 71 × 89
Purchased from the artist March 1993
P6162

HEAD Tim B 1946
Deluge 1985

Cibachrome print, 93.5 × 120.5
One of an edition of three
Purchased from Nicola Jacobs Gallery October 1990
P5833

KILLIP Chris[8] B 1946
From **In Flagrante** 1975–87

12 untitled silver bromide prints
11 prints: each 66 × 74; one print (P5609) 74 × 66 (framed)
Purchased from the artist June 1988
P5598–P5609 (P5600 illustrated)

KNORR Karen[10] B 1954
From **Country Life** 1983–85

A Young Nobleman's Introduction to Knowledge.
Silver print, with text, 63.5 × 53.5 (framed)
Purchased from the artist March 1993
P6163

HAUGHEY Anthony B 1963
From **Home** 1991–92

Two untitled C-type colour prints
Each 48 × 48
Purchased from the artist March 1993
P6172 (illustrated), P6173
(P6173 colour plate 50)

HEAD Tim B 1946
Toxic Lagoon 1987

Cibachrome print, 122.5 × 159.5
One of an edition of three
Purchased from Nicola Jacobs Gallery October 1990
P5834 (colour plate 51)

KIPPIN John[9] B 1950
(NOSTALGIA FOR THE FUTURE) North Seaton, Northumberland 1988

C-type colour print, with screenprinted text, 71 × 89
Purchased from the artist March 1993
P6161 (colour plate 52)

LONG Richard B 1945
England 1968

Black and white photograph, with text 83.8 × 114.3
Purchased from Anthony d'Offay Gallery June 1989
P5640

 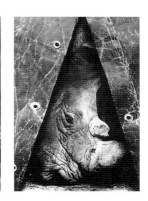

Long Richard B 1945
Circle in Africa 1978

Black and white photograph, with text
83.8 × 114.3
Purchased from Anthony d'Offay
Gallery June 1989
P5641

Mahr Mari B 1941
I would like to go on Safari 1989

Cibachrome prints (triptych – each
print framed separately)
Each 58.2 × 40.1
Purchased from Zelda Cheatle Gallery
September 1989
P5646A–C

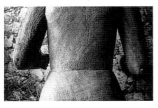 

Mahr Mari B 1941
Historical Grievances 1988

A work comprising a sequence of six
Cibachrome prints (framed separately)
Each 49.3 × 75.2
Purchased from The Photographers'
Gallery March 1991
P5903A–F

Meecham Charles B 1950
Middle Dean Wood 1985–86

A work comprising a sequence of nine
untitled Ilfochrome classic prints
(framed separately)
Each 40.6 × 50.8
Purchased from the artist April 1992
P6057A–I

MOORE Raymond[11] 1920–1987
From Murmurs at Every Turn
1959–80

Eight silver prints
Purchased from Birksted Gallery,
London February 1985
P5015–P5018, P5021–P5024
(P5023 illustrated)

Alderney 1966

26.4 × 35
Edition 3/7
P5023

Pembrokeshire 1967

25.7 × 35.5
Edition 2/7
P5018

Kilkenny 1971

21.9 × 29.3
Edition 1/7
P5016

Wiltshire 1975

25.3 × 35.3
Edition 2/7
P5015

Fletchertown 1977

21.3 × 29
Edition 2/7
P5017

Flimby 1977

28.8 × 27.1
Edition 2/7
P5021

Maryport 1980

27.1 × 28
Edition 1/7
P5022

Harrington 1980

28 × 36.2
Edition 1/7
P5024

MOORE Raymond 1920–1987
From Every So Often 1976–83

Two silver prints
Purchased from Birksted Gallery,
London February 1985
P5019 (illustrated), P5020

Allonby 1981

25.7 × 34.5
Edition 1/7
P5019

Flimby 1983

26.4 × 35.5
Edition 2/7
P5020

O'DONNELL Ron B 1952
**The Antechamber of Rameses V
in the Valley of the Kings** 1985

Cibachrome print, 80.5 × 103
Purchased from The Photographers'
Gallery July 1986
P5397 (colour plate 53)

O'DONNELL Ron B 1952
**From Woodland Animals
Series I–IV** 1985

Woodland Animal III

Cibachrome print, 38.1 × 47.7
Purchased from The Photographers'
Gallery July 1986
P5399

O'DONNELL Ron B 1952
Chip Dinner 1985

Cibachrome print, 38.1 × 47.7
Purchased from The Photographers'
Gallery July 1986
P5400

O'DONNELL Ron B 1952
Odeon 2 1985

Cibachrome print, 40 × 51.1
Purchased from the artist June 1987
P5500

O'DONNELL Ron B 1952
Cameo Robot 1985

Cibachrome print, 40.5 × 51.5
Purchased from the artist June 1987
P5501

O'DONNELL Ron B 1952
Still Life is Alive & Kicking 1986

Cibachrome print, 103 × 80.5
Purchased from The Photographers'
Gallery July 1986
P5398

O'DONNELL Ron B 1952
Adam and Eve 1989

Cibachrome print, 152.3 × 122
Purchased from the artist November
1989
P5695

O'DONNELL Ron B 1952
Bed of Osiris 1989

Cibachrome print, 122 × 152.3
Purchased from the artist November
1989
P5696

SEAR Helen B 1955
NATURAL HABITAT
living room 1989

C-type colour prints (triptych – each
print framed separately)
Each 91.5 × 91.5
Purchased from Zelda Cheatle Gallery
April 1990
P5810A–C

PALMER Roger B 1946
Ampersand 1989

Eight frames, each containing a silver
print and a text/drawing (displayed in
four parts; each with an upper and
lower frame)
Print and drawing: each 69.8 × 92.5;
framed 105 × 223
Presented by the artist October 1994
P6374A–H (P6374A, P6374B illustrated)

PARR Martin B 1952
From **Home and Abroad** 1983–93

**Bongo Burger Bar, Windsor Safari
Park** 1992

C-type colour print, 42.8 × 52.7
Purchased from the artist April 1994
P6268

SEAR Helen B 1955
PROJECTED INTERIORS
sitting room 1989

C-type colour prints (diptych – each
print framed separately)
Each 104.2 × 104.2
Purchased from Zelda Cheatle Gallery
April 1990
P5813A, P5813B (colour plate 54)

PARR Martin[12] B 1952
From **The Last Resort
Photographs of New Brighton**
1983–85

Six untitled Evercolor prints
Purchased from the artist November
1986
P5434–P5439 (P5437 illustrated)

Untitled	**Untitled**
50.8 × 61	30.5 × 40.6
P5434	P5437
Untitled	**Untitled**
50.8 × 61	30.5 × 40.6
P5435	P5438
Untitled	**Untitled**
30.5 × 40.6	30.5 × 40.6
P5436	P5439

REAS Paul[13] B 1955
From **Flogging a Dead Horse**
1989–93

Two C-type colour prints
Purchased from the artist March 1993
P6174, P6175 (P6175 illustrated)

**Beamish Open Air Museum, 'The
Northern Experience'**

50.8 × 61
P6174

**'Thomas Hardy Country', Old
Sarum**

66 × 76.2
P6175

SEAWRIGHT Paul B 1965
From **Sectarian Murder** 1989

Two C-type colour prints with text
Each 94.5 × 74.2 (framed)
Purchased from the artist March 1993
P6176, P6177 (P6177 illustrated)
P6176 (colour plate 55)

Saturday 9th June 1973

'A Sixty year old man was found shot
three times in the head in Ballysillan
Playground. The area showed signs of a
struggle.'
P6176

Monday 30th December 1974

'A 17 year old boy was duck shooting on
the shores of Belfast Lough. Four men
approached him demanding he hand
his shotgun over. They then shot him in
the head before leaving with the
weapon.'
P6177

SOUTHAM Jem[14] B 1950
From **Paintings of the West of Cornwall** 1982–86

Four C-type colour prints
Each 40.5 × 50.6
Purchased from the artist December 1986
P5470–P5473 (P5470 illustrated)

Marks Bakery, Camborne

P5470

Ocean Fresh Fish Shop, Penzance

P5471

Bar Capri, St. Ives

P5472

Cove Café, St. Agnes

P5473

SOUTHAM Jem B 1950
From **The Red River** 1982–88

Two C-type colour prints
Each 40.6 × 50.8
Purchased from the artist March 1993
P6164, P6165 (P6165 illustrated)

Harvest Festival, Condurrow Chapel

P6164

Roseworthy Stream and the Red River meet, Ponsbrittal

P6165

STEELE-PERKINS Chris B 1947
From a series taken at London Neighbourhood Festivals 1975–77

15 untitled silver bromide prints
Printed to a standard size: portrait 40.5 × 27; landscape 27 × 40.5
Purchased from the artist February 1978
These works formed part of the circulating exhibition *The British at Play Photographs by Chris Steele-Perkins, Homer Sykes and Patrick Ward*, which toured 1978–1984
(P4811 illustrated)
See Appendix for individual entries

SULTER Maud[15] B 1960
From **Syrcas** 1993
Duval et Dumas

Matt laminated C-type colour prints (diptych – each print framed separately): each 76.2 × 101.6
One of an edition of five
Presented by the artist September 1994
P6291A, P6291B

SYKES Homer[16] B 1949
From **Once a Year Some Traditional British Customs**
1973–77

15 silver bromide prints
Printed to a standard size: portrait 40.5 × 27; landscape 27 × 40.5
Purchased from the artist February 1978
These works formed part of the circulating exhibition *The British at Play Photographs by Chris Steele-Perkins, Homer Sykes and Patrick Ward*, which toured 1978–1984
(P4828 illustrated)
See Appendix for individual entries

WARD Patrick[17] B 1937
From **Wish You Were Here - the English at Play** 1973–76

15 silver bromide prints
Printed to a standard size: portrait 40.5 × 27; landscape 27 × 40.5
Purchased from the artist February 1978
These works formed part of the circulating exhibition *The British at Play Photographs by Chris Steele-Perkins, Homer Sykes and Patrick Ward*, which toured 1978–1984
(P4853 illustrated)
See Appendix for individual entries

WENTWORTH Richard B 1947
From **Making Do and Getting By** 1972 –

Eight colour prints made from transparencies
Printed to a standard size: portrait 11 × 7; landscape 7 × 11
Purchased from the artist April 1987
P5492–P5499 (P5494 illustrated)

Bermondsey, London 1976

P5494

New York 1978

P5492

King's Cross, London 1978

P5496

Normandy, France 1980

P5497

King's Cross, London 1980

P5499

Islington, London 1982

P5495

Islington, London 1982

P5498

Beijing 1986

P5493

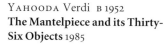

YAHOODA Verdi B 1952
The Mantelpiece and its Thirty-Six Objects 1985

Black and white film printed on colour paper, 20 × 390 overall size
Purchased from the artist October 1986
P5426 (detail)

APPENDIX

The following photographs originally formed three circulating exhibitions organised by the British Council's General Exhibitions Department –*Bill Brandt Photographs; Wales Black and White: Photographs by David Hurn*; and *The British at Play Photographs by Chris Steele-Perkins, Homer Sykes and Patrick Ward.* They were transferred to Fine Arts Department in April 1984 and incorporated into the Collection.

BRANDT Bill 1904–1983
Bill Brandt Photographs
For ease of reference, these photographs have been grouped according to subject

London in the Thirties

Tic-Tac men at Ascot Races 1932
P4700

Evening in Kew Gardens 1932
P4706

Parlourmaid and under-parlourmaid ready to serve dinner 1933
P4708

After the theatre, taxi in Lower Regent Street 1934
P4711

Young housewife, Bethnal Green 1937
P4703

Parlourmaid preparing a bath before dinner 1937
P4707

Bedroom in West Ham 1937
P4710

Late evening in the kitchen 1938
P4698

A resident of Putney 1938
P4702

Cocktails in a Surrey garden 1938
P4705

Parlourmaid at a window in Kensington 1939
P4967

Battersea Bridge 1939
P4701

East End girl, dancing the Lambeth Walk 1939
P4704

Drawing-Room in Mayfair 1939
P4709

Northern Towns in the Depression of the 1930s 1937

A snicket in Halifax
P4699

Ironworks, Sheffield
P4712

Coal-searchers near Heworth, Tyneside pithead train in the distance
P4713

Halifax
P4714

East Durham coal-miner just home from the pit
P4715

Coal-miner's bath, Chester-le-Street, Durham
P4716

Northumbrian miner at his evening meal
P4717

Coal-searcher going home to Jarrow
P4718

Blackout Nights of the London Blitz 1940

People sheltering in the tube, Elephant and Castle Underground Station
P4719

Crowded improvised air-raid shelter in Liverpool Street tube tunnel
P4720

Moonlit Regency balcony, Downshire Hill, Hampstead
P4721

Literary Britain

West Wycombe Park 1943
after Sir Francis Dashwood
P4688

The Roman Wall (looking eastward across Crag Loch to Hotbank) 1943
after Rudyard Kipling
P4695

Haworth Churchyard 1944
after the Brontës
P4691

Top Withens, West Riding, Yorkshire 1945
after Emily Brontë
P4692

Gull's nest, late on mid-summer night, Isle of Skye 1947
after James Boswell
P4735

Flint Cottage, Boxhill c.1948
after George Meredith
P4696

Barbary Castle, Marlborough Downs, Wiltshire 1948
after Richard Jefferies
P4694

Portraits

Dylan Thomas at the 'Salisbury' Public House 1941
P4723

Robert Graves in his cottage at Churston, Devon 1941
P4724

Edith and Osbert Sitwell beneath the Family Group by Sargent, Renishaw Hall, Derbyshire 1945
P4722

Portrait of Marjorie Brandt, Campden Hill, London 1949
P4727

Portrait of a young girl, Eaton Place, London 1955
P4726

Jean Dubuffet's right eye 1960
P4732

Jean Arp's right eye 1960
P4733

Harold Pinter, Battersea 1961
P4725

Francis Bacon walking on Primrose Hill, London 1963
P4731 (illustrated)

Antonio Tapies' left eye 1964
P4734

Malcolm Muggeridge, Robertsbridge 1966
P4730

J B Priestley in his garden at Alveston 1969
P4729

Portrait of Man Ray, Vence, Alpes-Maritimes 1970
P4728

Perspective of Nudes

Campden Hill, London 1948
P4737

Campden Hill, London 1949
P4738

London 1952
P4739

East Sussex Coast 1953
P4740

Vastérival, Normandy 1954
P4741

Campden Hill, London 1956
P4742

East Sussex Coast 1957
P4743

St. John's Wood, London 1957
P4744

London 1959
P4745

Baie des Anges, France 1959
P4746

The following works are not associated with an identified body of work:

Figurehead in a garden, Isles of Scilly 1934
P4687

Stonehenge under snow 1947
P4736 (This image was used as the front cover of *Picture Post* 19 April 1947)

The Pilgrim's Way, Kent 1950
P4693

Caligo in a bush near Taxo d'Aval 1961
P4869

Seventeenth century sculpture, Bomarzo near Rome 1965
P4690

HURN David B 1934
Wales Black and White 1971–73

Tylorstown
P6228

Coach party, Aberavon Beach
P6229

Elan Valley
P6230

Rock Pool, Llantwit Major
P6231

International Eisteddfod, Llangollen
P6232

Student grant Demonstration
P6233

Pigeon training, Powys
P6234

Country cottage, Upper Chapel
P6235

The Last Parade, Mayor's Procession, Llanidloes
P6236

Pantomime Horse Competition, Powys
P6237

Pig Race, County Rally, Brecon
P6238

Miners' Gala, Cardiff
P6239

Savoy Ballroom, Bargoed
P6240

Barry Zoo
P6241

Sheep dipping, Ty-Mawr
P6242

Throw a flour-bag, Donkey Derby, Penarth
P6243

Eisteddfod, Upper Chapel
P6244

Barry Island beach
P6245

Porth Cadlan, Caernarvon
P6246

Princess Margaret Rose
P6247

Regimental Museum, Royal Welch Fusiliers, Caernarvon Castle
P6248

Jazz Band, Merthyr Tydfil
P6249

Kite flying, Brecon Beacons
P6250

Artillery range, Epynt
P6251 (illustrated)

Pen-y-lan, Cardiff
P6252

Sing song, Sennybridge
P6253

Housing estate pond, Cardiff
P6254

Caerphilly Castle
P6255

Sea front, West Wales
P6256

Aber Eiddy, Old Man and Creation
P6257

Resting in Tenby
P6258

Black Mountain pony
P6259

Antique hearse, Gwent
P6260

Caravan site, East Wales
P6261

Sarah in Abertillery
P6262

Adrian Street, wrestler, Rhyl
P6263

Rhossili Bay
P6264

Ghost Train at Porthcawl
P6265

The British at Play Photographs by Chris Steele-Perkins, Homer Sykes and Patrick Ward

STEELE-PERKINS Chris B 1947

15 untitled silver bromide prints taken at London Neighbourhood Festivals 1975–77

P4809–P4823 (P4811 illustrated)

SYKES Homer B 1949

Prints taken 1973–77

The Haxey Hood Game, Haxey, Humberside
6 January
P4826

Westminster School Pancake Greaze, Westminster, London
Shrove Tuesday
P4834

Bottle Kicking and Hare Pie Scrambling, Hallaton, Leicestershire
Easter Monday
P4838

The Minehead Hobby Horse, Minehead, Somerset
30 April–2 May
P4827

Gawthorpe May Day, Gawthorpe, Yorkshire
1 May
P4825

Garland Day, Castleton, Derbyshire
29 May
P4832

Pinner Fair, Pinner, Middlesex
Whit Wednesday
P4831

Cheese-rolling, Cooper's Hill, Gloucestershire
Spring Bank Holiday Monday
P4829

Bellerby Feast, Bellerby, North Yorkshire
Spring Bank Holiday Monday
P4830

The Glorious Fourth of June, Eton, Berkshire
Nearest Saturday
P4828 (illustrated)

The Election of the Mayor of Ock Street, Abingdon, Oxfordshire
Saturday nearest 19 June
P4836

The John Knill Ceremony, St. Ives, Cornwall 25 July, every five years
P4835

Bampton Mummers, Bampton, Oxfordshire
24 December
P4837

The Marshfield Paper Boys, Marshfield, Avon
26 December
P4833

Tar-barrel Parade, Allendale, Northumberland
31 December
P4824

WARD Patrick B 1937

Critical listener to the brass band at a sheep farmers' show at Wensleydale in Yorkshire 1973
P4846

Confrontation with a competitor at the Aylesbury County Show 1974
P4843

Huddling in the rain at Old Warden Aerodrome, near Biggleswade, at a flying display of vintage aeroplanes 1974
P4851

Sale of stuffed animals in North London. This rhinoceros was too large to get into the sale-room, and was being carefully guarded in the entrance hall 1975
P4839

Guardsmen crossing St. James's Park early on the morning of the Trooping of the Colour, to celebrate the Queen's birthday 1975
P4840

Visitors to Glyndebourne, a country house in Sussex where opera is performed during the summer, enjoying a picnic during the extended interval 1975
P4841

Eton schoolboys watching the Eton Wall Game, a special kind of rugby, which is being played against the other side of the wall 1975
P4842

Child entering an Adventure Playground at Biglands Grass, an open space in East London 1975
P4844

Leaders of a Sunday afternoon free dancing event for elderly people at Parsloes Park, in East London 1975
P4845

Photographer and model on the Serpentine Lido in London's Hyde Park 1975
P4848

Trying to survive the British weather in October, on the Golden Mile, at the seaside resort of Blackpool 1975
P4849

Motorcyclist practising his yoga in Hyde Park 1975
P4850

Winner of the Miss Bo-Peep competition receiving her prize from the Vicar at a country garden fête in Gloucestershire 1975
P4852

Drag show at the Vauxhall Tavern, a pub in South London famous for its drag shows 1975
P4853 (illustrated)

Members of the East Lancashire Whippet Racing Society chatting before a Sunday morning racing meet at Accrington in Lancashire 1976
P4847

The following list of monographs relates specifically to photographs in the British Council Collection which belong to an identified sequence, series, publication or exhibition.

1. *Inscape | John Blakemore*, introductory essay by Val Williams
(Zelda Cheatle Press Ltd., London, 1991)
The Stilled Gaze John Blakemore, introductions by John Banville and Judith Bumpus
(Zelda Cheatle Press Ltd., London, 1994)

2. *Bill Brandt Perspective of Nudes*, preface by Lawrence Durrell, introduction by Chapman Mortimer
(Bodley Head, London, 1961)
Shadow of Light Photographs by Bill Brandt, introductions by Cyril Connolly and Mark Haworth-Booth
(The Gordon Fraser Gallery Ltd., London and Bedford, 1977)
Nudes 1945-1980 Photographs by Bill Brandt, introduction by Michael Hiley
(The Gordon Fraser Gallery Ltd., London and Bedford, 1982)
Bill Brandt Portraits, introduction by Alan Ross
(The Gordon Fraser Gallery Ltd., London and Bedford; University of Texas Press, Austin, 1982)
London in the Thirties Bill Brandt
(The Gordon Fraser Gallery Ltd., London and Bedford, 1983; also published with an introduction by Mark Haworth-Booth, Pantheon Books, New York, 1984)
Literary Britain Photographed by Bill Brandt, with an introduction by John Hayward. Edited and with an afterword by Mark Haworth-Booth
(Victoria and Albert Museum in association with Hurtwood Press, Westerham, Kent, 1984; original edition, with an introduction by John Hayward, published by Cassell & Company Ltd., London, 1951)
Bill Brandt Behind the Camera Photographs 1928-1983, introductions by Mark Haworth-Booth, essay by David Mellor
(Phaidon Press Ltd., Oxford, 1985)

3. *Calum Colvin The Seven Deadly Sins and the Four Last Things*, introductory essay by Tom Normand
(Portfolio Gallery, Edinburgh, 1993)

4. *A Green & Pleasant Land Photographs by John Davies*, introduction by Michael Wood, essay by Rob Powell
(Cornerhouse Publications, Manchester, 1987)
Cross Currents John Davies, introductory essay by Ian Walker
(Ffotogallery, Cardiff in association with Cornerhouse Publications, Manchester, 1992)

5. *Two Blue Buckets Photographs by Peter Fraser*, text by Rupert Martin, afterword by Maureen O. Paley
This publication includes documentation on **The Valleys Project** and **Everyday Icons**
(Cornerhouse Publications, Manchester, 1988)

6. *Steelworks Consett, from Steel to Tortilla Chips by Julian Germain*, Photographs by Julian Germain, Tommy Harris, Don McCullin & the People of Consett, with text by David Lee, J H Watson, Hunter Davies, Martin Herron
(Why Not Publishing, London, 1990)

7. *Troubled Land The Social Landscape of Northern Ireland Photographs by Paul Graham*, texts by Declan McGonagle and Gerry Badger
(Grey Editions, London, with Cornerhouse Publications, Manchester, 1987)

8. *In Flagrante Chris Killip*, with an essay by John Berger & Sylvia Grant
(Martin Secker & Warburg Ltd., London, 1988)

9. *Nostalgia for the Future John Kippin Photographs 1988-1994*, introduction by David Chandler, essay by John Taylor
(The Photographers' Gallery, London, 1995)

10. *Marks of Distinction Karen Knorr*, introduction by Patrick Mauriès
(Thames and Hudson Ltd., London, 1991)

11. *Murmurs at Every Turn The Photographs of Raymond Moore*, introduction by Mark Haworth-Booth
(Travelling Light, London, 1981)
Every so Often Photographs by Raymond Moore, introduction by Clive Lancaster, edited by Neil Hanson
(BBC North East in association with Northern Arts and the Arts Council of Great Britain, 1983, published to accompany a film of the same title)

12. *The Last Resort Photographs of New Brighton by Martin Parr*, text by Ian Walker
(Promenade Press, Wallasey, 1986)
Martin Parr Home and Abroad, introduction by Ian McEwan
(Jonathan Cape, London, 1993)

13. *Flogging a Dead Horse Photographs by Paul Reas*, text by Stuart Cosgrove, afterword by Val Williams
(Cornerhouse Publications, Manchester, 1993)

14. *The Red River Photographs Jem Southam*, poem D M Thomas, essay Frank Turk & Jan Ruhrmund
(Cornerhouse Publications, Manchester, 1989)

15. *Syrcas Maud Sulter*, with an essay by Lubaina Himid
(Wrexham Library Arts Centre, Clwyd, 1994)

16. *Once a Year Some Traditional British Customs Homer Sykes*, introduction by Paul and Georgina Smith
(The Gordon Fraser Gallery Ltd., London and Bedford, 1977)

17. *Wish You Were Here – the English at Play Photographs by Patrick Ward*, introduction and commentary by James Cameron
(The Gordon Fraser Gallery Ltd., London and Bedford, 1977)

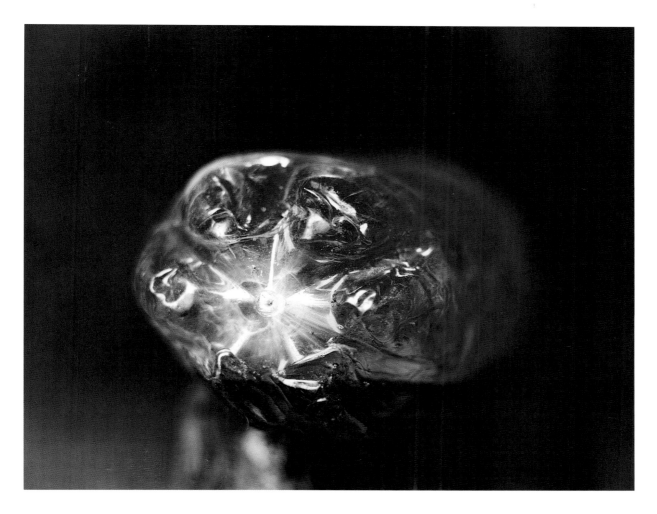

48 KEITH ARNATT
Untitled
From **Objects from a Rubbish
Tip** 1989–
P5697

49 CALUM COLVIN
Deaf Man's Villa 1989
P5827

50 ANTHONY HAUGHEY
Untitled
From **Home** 1991–92
P6173

51 TIM HEAD
Toxic Lagoon 1987
P5834

52 JOHN KIPPIN
**(NOSTALGIA FOR THE
FUTURE) North Seaton,
Northumberland** 1988
P6161

53 Ron O'Donnell
**The Antechamber of
Rameses V in the Valley of
the Kings** 1985
P5397

54 HELEN SEAR
PROJECTED INTERIORS
sitting room 1989
P5813A, P5813B

Saturday 9th June 1973

'A Sixty year old man was found shot three times in the head in Ballysillan Playground. The area showed signs of a struggle.'

55 PAUL SEAWRIGHT
   Saturday 9th June 1973
   from **Sectarian Murder** 1989
   P6176

PART V : **The Craft Collection**

Portrait of Muriel Rose
Reproduced with permission from
Holburne Museum and Crafts Study
Centre, Bath

The original ledger, detailing acquisitions for the Craft Collection, lists over 500 items, ranging from the hand crafted to the machine made.

Evidence of the British Council's interest and commitment to the purchase and display of craft works first appears in the Minutes of the Fine Arts (General) Committee meeting of September 1940. These record a resolve to mount an exhibition of fine British craftsmanship to visit 'the Dominions and certain foreign countries'. In 1942 the first major crafts exhibition was mounted. Planned and assembled by Muriel Rose in the Royal Library at Windsor Castle, the *Exhibition of Modern British Crafts* opened 20 May 1942 at the Metropolitan Museum of Art in New York.

It was a remarkable enterprise at a time when, as Sir Eric Maclagan, Director of the Victoria and Albert Museum and Chairman of the Fine Arts (General) Committee, observed in his introductory note to the catalogue: 'Everybody who can use his hands or hers, is using them for another purpose. Silk means parachutes, not embroidery; the guns can spare no iron; and the potteries are too busy with insulators to supply decorative tea services'. He goes on to point out that whereas 'in ordinary circumstances the British Council would have been able to choose from a wide field, and to commission special material for such a purpose, it has now had to content itself with what was available'.

Notwithstanding these and other problems (six tons of art objects convoyed across the Atlantic at the crest of the submarine war), the exhibition incorporated an extraordinary range, from 'Basic Crafts of the Soil' to ceramic ware by Bernard Leach. As one American reviewer commented, 'This is a highly diversified show, containing everything from those witches' brooms used in farm homes to the most elegant products of the Worshipful Company of Goldsmiths. The glass and pottery shown run the gamut from the squat but beautifully functional shapes to the exquisite and patrician'.

Works were arranged imaginatively, in constructed domestic interiors: Country Dining-Room, Country Bedroom, Town Dining-Room and Music Room. Each 'room' was furnished with an eye for detail – domestic pottery arranged on dressers, a jewel box and hairbrushes to hand on a dressing table, elegant place settings on a dining table designed by Eric Ravilious. It is from this exhibition that the earliest works in the Craft Collection date.

Fine Arts Department went on to show craft exhibitions in all parts of the globe. In 1946 it joined forces with the Rural Industries Bureau, the National Federation of Women's Institutes, and the Highland Home Industries to present the *Exhibition of Rural Handicrafts from Great Britain*, touring first in New Zealand (where it was seen by over 100,000 visitors) and later Australia. The exhibition contained only examples of handicrafts then commonly practised in the British countryside; a section was devoted to 'Thrift Crafts' with knitted and spun works from wool gathered from the hedgerows and fences, and dyed with gorse flowers, indigo and weld.

The Department was particularly fortunate in securing as Crafts and Industrial Design Officer the services and expertise of Muriel Rose. Her credentials were impeccable; she had spent five years (1922–27) assisting Dorothy Hutton to run the pioneering Three Shields Gallery in Holland Street, before launching, in 1928, her own highly successful venture, the Little Gallery. The Little Gallery prospered, promoting not only the work of outstanding British makers, but also that of Japanese makers, and ethnic crafts from communities in South

America, India, China, and Eastern and Western Europe. It attracted a wide range of clients, which included collectors, members of the artistocracy, and leading figures from artistic and society circles. Bernard Leach recalls in[1] *Beyond East and West* that Charles Laughton purchased 'many of the best pieces' from his exhibition at the Little Gallery, and consequently he and Muriel Rose were invited to dine with Laughton and his wife, Elsa Lanchester.[2] The Little Gallery closed in January 1940, and Muriel Rose subsequently joined the British Council, remaining until her retirement in 1957.

Initially, it had been British Council policy to purchase works solely for exhibition purposes. It was not until December 1948 that the Fine Arts (General) Committee agreed 'that any one of the following experts could be invited to collaborate with Miss Rose in the choice of purchases for this collection (the Permanent Collection of examples of Industrial Design and Crafts): Mr W B Honey, Mr Gordon Russell, Miss Catherine Cockerell, Miss Marianne Straub, Mrs R D Russell and Lady Sempill'. No sooner had this resolution been passed, than the indefatigable Muriel Rose visited an exhibition of Michael Cardew's work, held at his brother Philip's home in Regents Park Terrace. Garth Clark, writing in his portrait of Michael Cardew,[3] records that she 'wisely arrived before the exhibition was formally opened and acquired the best pieces for the British Council Collection, much to the dismay of the Victoria and Albert Museum'. Muriel Rose continued to acquire fine examples of work by Cardew, Coper, Leach, Rie and Whiting, as well as more utilitarian pieces for inclusion in exhibitions of British industrial design.

In the 1960s the Craft Collection was reappraised. It had suffered depredation through breakages, loss and worm damage. In 1960 the rustic items were presented to the Museum of Rural Life at the University of Reading, and in 1961 textiles and entire china services were sold to the Victoria and Albert Museum and the Whitworth Art Gallery, University of Manchester. In April 1972 four pieces of furniture were sold to Holburne Museum and Crafts Study Centre, Bath.

No further items were added to the Craft Collection until Muriel Wilson (Curator 1979–1984) acquired works to form the exhibition *Cloth Clay Wood* which toured extensively from 1987 to 1993. She later purchased a collection of jewellery to create the exhibition *All that glisters … New Jewellery in Britain*, mounted in 1992, and still on tour at the time of writing. More recent acquisitions have been made by Andrea Rose (Curator 1989–1993) – a representative group of glass and ceramic works for the new British Council offices in Prague, and eight key works by contemporary makers for display in the British Council's headquarters in Manchester.

There has been some retracing of footsteps; in 1992 examples of Wedgwood ware, designed by Eric Ravilious, were purchased to complement existing holdings of this artist's work. In 1993 teapots by Cliff, Cooper, Seeney and Tait were added to the Collection. These were acquired for a dual purpose – to create a lively and charming showcase display, and with a view to assembling an exhibition to celebrate that most British of activities, having a cup of tea. By happy coincidence, it was a 6¼ gallon teapot, designed by Michael Cardew for use at country tennis parties, which some 53 years ago so delighted the American reviewers of the British Council's first ever exhibition of crafts.

Notes

1. *Beyond East and West Memoirs, Portraits and Essays* by Bernard Leach (Faber and Faber, 1978) p 223
2. Property from the estate of the late Elsa Lanchester, sold 27 January 1988 at Christie's, London, included many examples of Bernard Leach's work.
3. *Michael Cardew A Portrait* by Garth Clark (Faber and Faber, 1978) p 53

Notes on the catalogue entries

The records relating to acquisitions 1945–1957 comprise a ledger and a card index, neither of which is contemporaneous. This catalogue is based on the 1957 ledger entries, which are the more complete. Works are variously prefixed AN, NZ, C and P. The prefix AN relates to works not recorded in the ledger at the time of purchase, but added to the inventory at a later date. (The Coronation Mug, 1952, from the revised Ravilious design is the only remaining work which retains this prefix). The prefix NZ applies to work included in the 1946 *Exhibition of Rural Handicrafts from Great Britain*; the Roman and Arabic numerals which follow indicate the position of the work within the exhibition. Works acquired 1945–1957 are prefixed C; works acquired since 1985 have the prefix P.

The ledger entries rarely date works, or record the purchase source, and it has therefore not been possible to date all the pieces in the Craft Collection. The designers of some of the manufactured items have also proved elusive. Any information which would enable these gaps to be filled would be most welcome.

The Craft Collection comprises three sections: studio pieces, production ware, and jewellery. Entries are arranged by maker in alphabetical order. Where a maker has more than one work in the Collection, the works are given in chronological order, with undated works preceding dated entries. Works of the same year are listed in British Council Collection accession number sequence, unless the actual day or month of completion is known.

1. Name of maker and date of birth (and death).

2. Title of work.

3. Date of work (where confirmed by the maker or by documentary evidence).

4. Medium.

5. Dimensions are given in centimetres.

6. Maker's mark or inscription.

7. Source and date of acquisition or accession date.

8. British Council Collection accession number.

BADROCKE Joyce B 1909
Two Figures

Machine-sewn polychrome embroidery, with sequins and beads, 46 × 35.5
Accessioned March 1948

C124

BAWDEN Edward 1903–1989
Wallpaper 'Lagoon' 1928 (also known as **'Waves'**)

Lithograph after linocut
87 × 54
Purchased from The Fine Art Society
March 1994

P6220 & P6221 [2 sheets]

BAYER Svend B 1946
Teapot 1991

Woodfired stoneware, Height 19
Purchased from The Craftsmen Potters
Association September 1992

P6094

BOLTON Janet B 1942
Bird and Cow 1985

Appliqué needlework in two panels
30 × 12.5 left panel; 29.2 × 13.4 right panel
Purchased from the maker October 1985

P5321

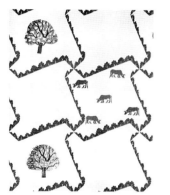

BAWDEN Edward 1903–1989
Wallpaper 'Tree and Cow' 1927

Lithograph after linocut
87 × 54
Purchased from The Fine Art Society
March 1994

P6218 & P6219 [2 sheets]
(colour plate 56)

BAWDEN Edward 1903–1989
Wallpaper 'Riviera' 1929

Autolithograph drawn by the artist
directly onto the plate, 87 × 55.8
Purchased from The Fine Art Society
September 1993

P6195

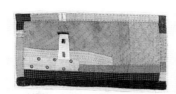

BOLTON Janet B 1942
The Lighthouse 1985

Appliqué needlework, 12.5 × 24
Purchased from the maker October 1985

P5319

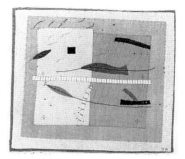

BOLTON Janet B 1942
A Gentle Breeze 1985

Appliqué needlework, 27 × 29.5
Sewn BRC: *J B*
Purchased from the maker October 1985

P5322

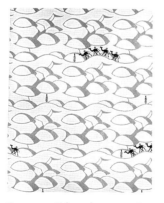

BAWDEN Edward 1903 – 1989
Wallpaper 'Sahara' 1928

Lithograph after linocut
87.5 × 54.9
Purchased from The Fine Art Society
September 1993; March 1994

P6194 & P6217 [2 sheets]

BAWDEN Edward 1903–1989
Wallpaper 'Knole Park' 1929

Lithograph after linocut
87 × 54
Purchased from The Fine Art Society
March 1994

P6215 & P6216 [2 sheets]

BOLTON Janet B 1942
Beehive, Bee and Yellow Leaf 1985

Appliqué needlework, 10.5 × 24
Purchased from the maker October 1985

P5320

BRADEN Norah B 1901
Lidded Jar

Buff stoneware, with two faint bands of
black enamel; lid with faint radiating
design in black enamel
Height 4.8
Purchased from Dunbar Hay Ltd.,
London September 1948

C180A (jar), C180B (lid)

BRADEN Norah B 1901
Lidded Jar

Buff stoneware, with two faint bands of black enamel; lid with faint radiating design in black enamel
Height 3.4
Purchased from Dunbar Hay Ltd., London September 1948
C181A (jar), C181B (lid)

CARDEW Michael[1] 1901–1983
Lidded Bowl *c.*1947

Stoneware, with grey glaze and fish design on lid in dark brown pigment
Diameter 17.3
Impressed on lid: (M)
Impressed on base of bowl: (M)
Accessioned December 1948
C287A (bowl), C287B (lid)

CARDEW Michael 1901–1983
Dessert Plate *c.*1947/48

Stoneware, with olive-green wood ash glaze and Vumé lily decoration
Diameter 20.3
Painted in glaze on base: (M) (⊗)
Accessioned December 1948
C289

CARDEW Michael 1901–1983
Jug *c.*1947/48

Stoneware, with dark olive-green glaze and brushed design in bright red iron
Height 15.9
Impressed on base: (M)
Accessioned December 1948
C294

BRITTON Alison B 1948
Black Leaning Pot 1990

High-fired earthenware, hand built, painted with slips and underglaze pigment under a clear matt glaze
Height 38.6
Inscribed on base: *Alison Britton '90*
Purchased from Oriel, Cardiff September 1991
P5969

CARDEW Michael 1901–1983
Teapot with Cane Handle[2] *c.*1947

Stoneware, with blue-grey glaze and brushed Vumé lily motif in iron pigment, Height 17.4
Impressed on base: (M) (⊗)
Accessioned December 1948
C292A (teapot), C292B (lid)

CARDEW Michael 1901–1983
Deep Bowl *c.*1947/48

Stoneware, with dark glaze and design in iron pigment, Diameter 22.9
Impressed on base: (M) (⊗)
Accessioned December 1948
C290

CARDEW Michael 1901–1983
Jug *c.*1947/48

Stoneware, with persimmon glaze and painted decoration, Height 12
Impressed on base: (M)
Accessioned December 1948
C295

BURKE Margaret B 1961
Bowl 1991

Etched glass, Diameter 26
Inscribed on base: *M Burke*
Purchased from Welsh Arts Council March 1992
P6036

CARDEW Michael 1901–1983
Jar[3] *c.*1947

Stoneware, with dark olive-green glaze and brushed Vumé lily motif in bright red iron, Height 24.1
Impressed on base: (M) (⊗)
Accessioned December 1948
C297

CARDEW Michael 1901–1983
Jug *c.*1947/48

Stoneware, with iron glaze and painted decoration, Height 20.3
Impressed on base: (M)
Accessioned December 1948
C293

CARDEW Michael 1901–1983
Large Plate[4,5] 1949

Stoneware, with grey-green glaze and brushed decoration of a bird
Diameter 27.4
Impressed on base: (M) (🐟)
Accessioned December 1950
C473

CARDEW Michael 1901–1983
Large Lidded Jar[5] *c.*1949/50

Stoneware, with blue-grey glaze and brushed iron decoration, Height 25.4
Impressed on base: [M] [symbol]
Accessioned December 1950
C468

CHANG Peter B 1944
Pepper Mill 1992

Acrylic, Height 46.5
Purchased from the maker March 1992
P6043

COPER Hans 1920–1981
Waisted Pot[7] *c.*1954

Buff and brown stoneware, with sgraffito decoration; burnished
Height 31.5
Impressed on base: [symbol]
Accessioned February 1956
C549 (colour plate 58)

DIXON Stephen B 1957
On the Brink 1990

Lead glazed earthenware, press moulded lidded vessel, with sprigged and modelled details
Height 40.7
Inscribed on base: *Stephen Dixon Maker*; inside lid: *The World Turned September Nineteen Ninety*
Purchased from Anatol Orient October 1991
P5971

CARDEW Michael 1901–1983
Bowl[5] *c.*1949/50

Stoneware, with grey-green glaze and brushed decoration of a bird
Diameter 24.7
Impressed on base: [M] [symbol]
Accessioned December 1950
C469 (colour plate 57)

CHATWIN Peter B 1945 :
MARTIN Pamela B 1949
Bowl 1988

Sycamore veneer, Width 59
Purchased from the makers February 1989
P5622

COPER Hans 1920–1981
Pot[8] *c.*1955

Stoneware, with sgraffito decoration through manganese, with a lighter band at the neck; burnished, Diameter 33.8
Impressed on base: [symbol]
Accessioned February 1956
C548 (colour plate 58)

COPER Hans 1920–1981
see also RIE Lucie : COPER Hans

FINCH Ray B 1914
Cider Jar (1½ Gallon)[10] *c.*1945/46[‡]

Earthenware, with trailed slip decoration, Height 31
Impressed on edge of base: [symbol] [symbol]
Accessioned 1945/46
NZ.XIII.4

CHANG Peter B 1944
Salt Mill 1992

Acrylic, Height 46
Purchased from the maker March 1992
P6042

COPER Hans 1920–1981
Bowl[6] 1952

Stoneware, manganese with light vertical ribbing and spiral incised decoration through pigment to cream body; foot and lower part of bowl pigmented but not glazed, Height 13.3
Impressed on base: [symbol]
Accessioned November 1953
C528

CROMPTON Rebecca 1910–1947
An Easter Egg[9] *c.*1938[†]

Silk embroidery on gauze, with silver metal threads and sequins, 38 × 49
Accessioned March 1946
C47

FINCH Ray B 1914
Bowl[10] *c.*1945/46[‡]

Earthenware, with trailed slip decoration, Diameter 22
Impressed on edge of base: [symbol] [symbol]
Accessioned 1945/46
NZ.XIV.9

FINCH Ray B 1914
Cider Jar (1½ Gallon)[10] *c*.1945/46
Earthenware, with trailed slip
decoration, Height 31.5
Impressed on edge of base: 🄟 🄵
Accessioned April 1946
C90

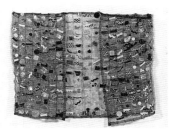

FREEMAN Susie B 1956
Sleeveless Jacket 1985
Knitted nylon monofilament, with
sequins, ric-rac, braid, buttons,
trimmings and ribbons, Length 52
Purchased from Aspects Gallery
October 1985
P5312

GARDINER Edward 1880–1958
Bedales Chair
From the original design by Ernest
Gimson (1864–1919), used for the
Memorial Library, Bedales School,
Hampshire
Ash with rush seat, Height 96.5
Accessioned October 1953
C513

HENDERSON Ewen B 1934
Pot 1986
Oxidised stoneware, bone china and
porcelain, Height 58
Purchased from British Crafts Centre
March 1986
P5349

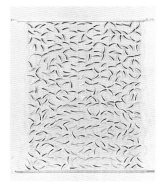

FREEMAN Susie B 1956
Gold Fish Hanging 1985
Knitted nylon monofilament, with
gold fish-shaped sequins, 66 × 50
Purchased from Aspects Gallery
October 1985
P5310

FREEMAN Susie B 1956
Pyjama Set 1985
Knitted nylon monofilament, with
Lurex and satin ribbon off-cuts
Jacket: length 66; Pants: length 69
Purchased from Aspects Gallery
February 1985
P5418

GARDINER Edward 1880–1958
Clissett Chair
From a design modified by Ernest
Gimson from the traditional design of
Philip Clissett (1817–1913)
Ash with rush seat, Height 88.9
Accessioned October 1953
C514

HOWARD Constance B 1910
Glass Bird[11] *c*.1945/46
Appliqué polychrome embroidery, with
sequins, beads and ric-rac, 48 × 41.5
Accessioned March 1946
C52

FREEMAN Susie B 1956
Sea-Shell Cowl 1985
Knitted nylon monofilament, with sea-
shells and small pebbles, Diameter 27
Purchased from Aspects Gallery
October 1985
P5311

FRITSCH Elizabeth B 1940
**Counterpoint Vase with Collision
of Particles** 1991
Hand built stoneware, decorated with
precise geometric patterns, Height 29.3
Purchased from the maker December
1991
P6005

GARDINER Edward 1880–1958
Clissett Armchair
From a design modified by Ernest
Gimson from the traditional design of
Philip Clissett
Ash with rush seat, Height 88.9
Accessioned October 1953
C515

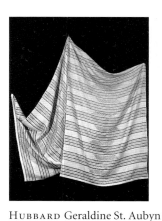

HUBBARD Geraldine St. Aubyn
B 1946
Inlay Shawl 1985
Handwoven and dyed silk, 243 × 75
Purchased from the maker October 1985
P5327

HUBBARD Geraldine St. Aubyn
B 1946
Kimono 1985

Handwoven and dyed silk
Length 108
The maker's name is printed on the
inside of the collar
Purchased from the maker October 1985
P5328

KAYE Margaret B 1912
Lion[12] c.1945/46

Appliqué polychrome embroidery, with
fulled wool, velvet, organza, sequins
and copper sheet, 48 × 58
Accessioned March 1946
C53

KEELER Walter B 1942
Teapot c.1986–87

Light grey-blue saltglazed stoneware
Height 13.8
Impressed beneath handle: ⊚
Purchased from Contemporary Applied
Arts February 1993
P6138

KEELER Walter B 1942
Teapot c.1989

Grey-blue saltglazed stoneware
Height 16
Impressed by handle: ⊚
Purchased from Welsh Arts Council
March 1992
P6031

HUBBARD Geraldine St. Aubyn
B 1946
Narrow Scarf 1985

Handwoven and dyed silk and wool
164 × 28
Purchased from the maker October 1985
P5329

KEELER Walter[13] B 1942
Bowl 1985

Dark grey-green saltglazed stoneware
Diameter 22
Impressed on both sides of lower rim: ⊚
Purchased from Collection Gallery,
Ledbury October 1985
P5307

KEELER Walter B 1942
Jug 1988

Grey-blue saltglazed stoneware
Height 9.3
Impressed on both sides of lower rim: ⊚
Purchased from Contemporary Applied
Arts March 1988
P5587

KEELER Walter B 1942
Teapot c.1989

Dark grey-green saltglazed stoneware
Height 13.8
Impressed beneath handle: ⊚
Purchased from Contemporary Applied
Arts February 1993
P6139

HUBBARD Geraldine St. Aubyn
B 1946
Wide Scarf 1985

Handwoven and dyed silk
167 × 39
Purchased from the maker October 1985
P5330

KEELER Walter B 1942
Lidded Jar 1985

Dark grey-green saltglazed stoneware
Height 34
Impressed on lower rim: ⊚
Purchased from The Craftsmen Potters
Association October 1985
P5313

KEELER Walter B 1942
Teapot 1988–89

Dark grey-green saltglazed stoneware
Height 25
Impressed on both sides, immediately
beneath upper rim: ⊚
Purchased from the maker February
1991
P5867

KEELER Walter B 1942
Jug 1989–91

Grey-blue saltglazed stoneware
Height 19
Impressed at base of handle: ⊚
Purchased from Welsh Arts Council
March 1992
P6032

KEELER Walter B 1942
Jug 1990

Grey-blue saltglazed stoneware
Height 15.5
Impressed by handle: ⊚
Purchased from Contemporary Applied
Arts March 1992
P6048

KEY Ray B 1942
Box 1990

Rio rosewood and burr thuya
Diameter 7.1
Engraved on base: *90116 Rio Rosewood
Burr Thuya Ray Key*
Purchased from the maker October
1990
P5817

LEACH Bernard 1887–1979
Large Jar with Handle[15] 1945

Stoneware, decorated on the front with
an embossed cross motif, and covered
with a speckled white-grey glaze
Height 38
Impressed at base beneath handle: ⊛ 🅱🅛
Purchased from Berkeley Galleries,
London July 1946
C91 (colour plate 60)

LEACH Bernard 1887–1979
Large Jar c.1948–52

Stoneware, speckled grey-brown
ground, with **Tree of Life** decoration
Height 31.8
Impressed on base: ⊛ 🅱🅛
Accessioned October 1952
C501 (colour plate 61)

KEY Ray B 1942
Bowl 1986

Natural topped burr mulberry
Diameter 25.7
Purchased from the maker August 1986
P5414

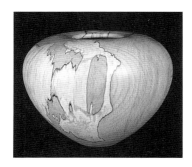

KEY Ray B 1942
Vessel 1990

Spalted beech, Height 11.5
Engraved on base: *89069 Spalted Beech
Ray Key*
Purchased from the maker October
1990
P5818

LEACH Bernard 1887–1979
Jug c.1946

Stoneware, with blue-grey glaze
Height 16.5
Impressed at base beneath handle: ⊛ 🅱🅛
Accessioned March 1947
C218

LEACH Bernard 1887–1979
Bowl c.1948–52

Stoneware, with tenmoku glaze and
brushed iron decoration, Diameter 10.8
Impressed on base: ⊛ 🅱🅛
Accessioned October 1952
C502

KEY Ray B 1942
Platter 1986

Fiddleback sycamore, Diameter 48
Stamped on base: *Ray Key*
Purchased from the maker August 1986
P5417

LEACH Bernard 1887–1979
Lidded Box[14] c.1942

Flat stoneware rectangular box, with
blue-green glaze, decorated on lid with
rust-brown lines, 3.2 × 11 × 6.4
Impressed on base: ⊛ 🅱🅛
Accessioned October 1952
C505

LEACH Bernard 1887–1979
Jug[16] 1948

Stoneware, with grey-green glaze
breaking to olive-brown, with red iron
splashes; medieval shape, Height 26.7
Impressed at base beneath handle: ⊛ 🅱🅛
Purchased from The Arts and Crafts
Exhibition Society's exhibition held at
the Guildhall March 1948
C123

LEACH Bernard 1887–1979
Bowl[17] c.1948–52

Stoneware, with leaf design decoration
in grey-green through a brown glaze
Diameter 10.5
Impressed on base: ⊛
Accessioned October 1952
C504

LEACH POTTERY, ST. IVES[18]

LEACH POTTERY
Bowl[‡]
Stoneware, with black glazed interior
Diameter 24.5
Impressed on base: ⊕
Accessioned 1945/46
NZ.XIII.19

LEACH POTTERY
Cream Jug
Stoneware, with tenmoku glaze
Height 7.7
Impressed at base beneath handle: ⊕
Accessioned March 1947
C214

LEACH POTTERY
Large Jug
Stoneware, with tenmoku glaze
Height 20.3
Impressed at base beneath handle: ⊕
Accessioned June 1950
C412

LEACH POTTERY
Butter Dish and Lid
Porcellaneous ware, with celadon glaze
Height 4.1
Impressed at base: ⊕
Accessioned June 1950
C418

LEACH POTTERY
Beaker
Stoneware, with grey glaze, lower part
unglazed, Height 10
Impressed in lower unglazed area: ⊕
Accessioned March 1947
C211

LEACH POTTERY
Jam Pot and Lid
Porcellaneous ware, with celadon glaze
and oak leaf decoration on lid
Height 7.4
No markings
Accessioned March 1947
C217

LEACH POTTERY
Milk Jug
Porcellaneous ware, with dark brown
glaze, Height 10
Impressed at base beneath handle: ⊕
Accessioned June 1950
C416

LEACH POTTERY
Cylindrical Vase
Stoneware, with blue-green glaze
Height 6.9
Impressed at base: ⊕
Accessioned June 1950
C425

LEACH POTTERY
Pint Beer Mug
Stoneware, with grey-green glaze
Height 12
Impressed on base: ⊕
Accessioned March 1947
C212

LEACH POTTERY
Pint Beer Mug
Stoneware, with tenmoku glaze
Height 12
Impressed at base beneath handle: ⊕
Accessioned June 1950
C409

LEACH POTTERY
Sugar Basin
Porcellaneous ware, with celadon glaze
Diameter 11.2
Impressed on base: ⊕
Accessioned June 1950
C417

LEACH POTTERY
Beaker
Stoneware, with tenmoku glaze
Height 9.2
Impressed on base: ⊕
Accessioned June 1950
C429

McLEAN Bruce B 1944
Jug 1987

Earthenware, painted with coloured glazes, Height 87
Purchased from Anthony d'Offay Gallery March 1987
P5486

MALONE Kate B 1959
Starfish in the Belly of a Sea Urchin 1989

Stoneware, decorated with coloured glazes, Diameter 28
Purchased from the maker March 1990
P5801 (colour plate 63)

MOORE Simon B 1959
Stacking Bowl 1991

Sandblasted glass, Diameter 27
Inscribed on base: *Glass Works*
Purchased from Welsh Arts Council March 1992
P6035

NEWELL Steven B 1948
Triangular Decanter 1991

Sandblasted glass
Height 43 (with stopper)
Inscribed on side: *Newell*
Purchased from Welsh Arts Council March 1992
P6037

McNICOLL Carol B 1943
Coffee Set 1991

Earthenware, painted with coloured glazes
Tray, coffee jug and six cups
Tray: 10 × 140 × 29
Each cup: height 7.6
Jug: height 29
Purchased from Welsh Arts Council March 1992
P6033 (colour plate 62)

MALONE Kate B 1959
Starfish Pie Dish 1992

Stoneware, decorated with coloured glazes, Diameter 43
Purchased from the maker May 1992
P6003

MOORE Simon B 1959
Ship's Decanter 1991

Glass, Height 25.5 (with stopper)
Inscribed on base: *Glass Works*
Purchased from Welsh Arts Council March 1992
P6040

NEWELL Steven B 1948
Jug 1991

Glass, with sandblasted base, Height 20
Inscribed on handle: *Newell*
Purchased from Welsh Arts Council March 1992
P6038

McNICOLL Carol B 1943
Fruit Bowl 1992

Earthenware, painted with coloured glazes, Height 23
Signed on base: *Carol McNicoll*
Purchased from the maker May 1992
P6006

MOORE Simon B 1959
Stacking Bowl 1991

Sandblasted glass, Diameter 23
Inscribed on base: *Glass Works*
Purchased from Welsh Arts Council March 1992
P6034

MOORE Simon B 1959
Decanter 1991

Glass, Height 31 (with stopper)
Inscribed on base: *Glass Works*
Purchased from Welsh Arts Council March 1992
P6041

NEWELL Steven B 1948
Jug 1991

Sandblasted glass, Height 20
Inscribed on handle: *Newell*
Purchased from Welsh Arts Council March 1992
P6039

NICZEWSKI Peter B 1948
Bowl 1985

Inlaid wood and dyed veneers
12 × 45.4 × 12
Inscribed on base: *P NICZEWSKI*
Purchased from British Crafts Centre
October 1985
P5331

PARTRIDGE Jim B 1953
Goblet 1985

Scorched burr oak, Height 18
Purchased from British Crafts Centre
October 1985
P5315

PARTRIDGE Jim B 1953
Bowl on Three Legs 1985

Scorched burr oak, Diameter 14
Purchased from British Crafts Centre
October 1985
P5318

PATEL Trupti B 1957
Ecstasy of the Potter I 1990

White unglazed earthenware, mounted
in a blockwood box, Diameter 51.5
Purchased from the maker June 1991
P5964

NICZEWSKI Peter B 1948
Shelf 1986

Dyed veneers, 50 × 57 × 11
Inscribed on reverse: *P NICZEWSKI*
Purchased from the maker April 1986
P5374

PARTRIDGE Jim B 1953
Flat Dish 1985

Scorched burr oak, Diameter 23.5
Purchased from British Crafts Centre
October 1985
P5316

PARTRIDGE Jim B 1953
Small Rectangular Bowl 1988

Scorched burr oak, 8 × 29 × 12
Purchased from the maker February
1989
P5623

RADSTONE Sara B 1955
Untitled Vessel 1986

Stoneware, with matt glaze, Height 21.5
Inscribed on base: *SR 86*
Purchased from Anatol Orient June
1986
P5381

O'NEILL Dennis B 1922
Beer Jar‡

Slipware, with sgraffito decoration of
hops and grapes, Height 33
Accessioned 1945/46
NZ.XIV.5

PARTRIDGE Jim B 1953
Dish on Foot 1985

Scorched burr oak, Diameter 20
Purchased from British Crafts Centre
October 1985
P5317

PARTRIDGE Jim B 1953
Spherical Bowl 1988

Scorched burr oak, Diameter 21
Stamped on base: *J. B. PARTRIDGE*
Purchased from the maker February
1989
P5624

RADSTONE Sara B 1955
Untitled Vessel 1986

Stoneware, with matt glaze, Height 32
Inscribed on base: 86
Purchased from Anatol Orient June
1986
P5382

RADSTONE Sara B 1955
Untitled Vessel 1986

Stoneware, with matt glaze, Height 23
Purchased from Anatol Orient June
1986
P5383

RAYBOULD Howard B 1946
Box 1985

Quebec pine, carved and coloured
10.5 × 27.5 × 14
Inscribed on base: *Sept 85*; stamped on
base: HJSR
Purchased from the maker April 1986
P5368

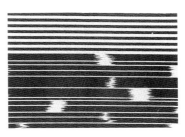

RESTIEAUX Mary B 1945
Group of seven Ikat Belts 1985

Silk, one belt: 114 × 15.5; two belts: each
150 × 10; four belts: each 153 × 15.5
Purchased from the maker February
1989
P5626A–G
(P5626A illustrated – detail)

RIE Lucie 1902–1995
Butter Dish

Porcelain, with black silky glaze and
white rim; bowl lipped, Width 10.8
Impressed on base: 🔲
Purchased from Berkeley Galleries,
London January 1950
C399

RADSTONE Sara B 1955
Untitled Vessel 1987–88

Stoneware, with matt glaze, Height 28
Purchased from Michaelson & Orient
May 1990
P5815

RAYBOULD Howard B 1946
Oval Platter 1986

Quebec pine, carved and coloured
Width 55.5
Stamped on base: HJSR
Purchased from the maker April 1986
P5366

RIE Lucie 1902–1995
Vase

White stoneware, with manganese
brushed onto rim and foot, Height 15.8
Impressed on base: 🔲
Purchased from Berkeley Galleries,
London January 1950
C397

RIE Lucie 1902–1995
Cup

Porcelain, vertical sgraffito lines
through thick and thin bands of
manganese on outside, transparent
glaze inside and over rim
Height 5.7
Impressed on base: 🔲
Purchased from Berkeley Galleries,
London January 1950
C400

RAYBOULD Howard B 1946
Still Life, Bowl of Fruit 1985

Quebec pine, carved and coloured
27 × 50 × 2.5
Carved on front: HJSR; stamped on
reverse: HJSR
Purchased from the maker April 1986
P5367

RAYBOULD Howard B 1946
Mirror 1986

Quebec pine, carved and coloured, and
mirror glass, 33.5 × 30 × 2.8
Purchased from the maker April 1986
P5369

RIE Lucie 1902–1995
Bottle with Squeezed Sides

Porcelain, with black silky glaze and
white rim, Height 15.2
Impressed on base: 🔲
Purchased from Berkeley Galleries,
London January 1950
C398

RIE Lucie 1902–1995
Shallow Dish

Porcelain, with white glaze and
manganese brushed onto rim
Diameter 10
Impressed on base: 🔲
Purchased from Berkeley Galleries,
London January 1950
C401

RIE Lucie 1902–1995
Bowl

Porcelain, with vertical looped sgraffito decoration through manganese Diameter 8
Impressed on base: 🔲
Purchased from Berkeley Galleries, London January 1950
C402

RIE Lucie 1902–1995
Vase

Stoneware, with white pitted and furrowed exterior, showing dark brown flecks, Height 29.8
Impressed on base: 🔲
Accessioned March 1957
C559

RIE Lucie 1902–1995
Bowl c.1949

Porcelain, with transparent glaze and manganese brushed onto inner rim and foot, Diameter 17.2
Impressed on base: 🔲
Purchased from Berkeley Galleries, London January 1950
C396

RIE Lucie 1902–1995
Bowl[20] 1949

Stoneware, with white glaze and unglazed brown rim, Diameter 12.7
Impressed on base: 🔲
Accessioned December 1950
C479

RIE Lucie 1902–1995
Cup

Porcelain, with translucent glaze and manganese brushed onto rim Height 6.3
Impressed on base: 🔲
Purchased from Berkeley Galleries, London January 1950
C403

RIE Lucie 1902–1995
Cup and Saucer

Stoneware, with black silky glaze and white rim, Cup: height 6.9; Saucer: diameter 13.8
Impressed on base of cup: 🔲 ; on base of saucer: 🔲
Accessioned March 1957
C563A (cup), C563B (saucer)

RIE Lucie 1902–1995
Bowl[19] 1949

Stoneware, with black silky glaze and white outer rim, Diameter 28
Impressed on base: 🔲
Accessioned December 1950
C475

RIE Lucie 1902–1995
Bowl[21] 1954

Porcelain, with 'American' yellow glaze and brown rim, Diameter 11
Impressed on base: 🔲
Accessioned June 1954
C537

RIE Lucie 1902–1995
Large Bowl

Stoneware, with white pitted and furrowed exterior, showing dark brown flecks, Diameter 30.5
Impressed on base: 🔲
Accessioned March 1957
C558

RIE Lucie 1902–1995
Cup and Saucer

Stoneware, with white glaze and brown foot, Cup: height 6.9; Saucer: diameter 14.6
Impressed on base of cup: 🔲 ; on base of saucer: 🔲
Accessioned March 1957
C564A (cup), C564B (saucer)

RIE Lucie 1902–1995
Beaker 1949

Porcelain, with white glaze and manganese at rim; asymmetrical Height 8.8
Impressed on base: 🔲
Accessioned December 1950
C478

RIE Lucie 1902–1995
Bowl[22] 1956

Porcelain, with bands of brown and white, Diameter 17.9
Impressed on base: 🔲
Accessioned February 1956
C545

RIE Lucie 1902–1995
Bowl[23] 1957

Porcelain, with sgraffito decoration through manganese, Diameter 25.3
Impressed on base: 🖃
Accessioned March 1957
C553 (colour plate 64)

RIE Lucie 1902–1995
Bowl[26] 1957

Porcelain, with 'American' yellow glaze and brown sgraffito band at rim
Diameter 21.2
Impressed on base: 🖃
Accessioned March 1957
C556 (colour plate 65)

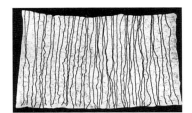

SALMON Janice B 1961
Floor Cover 1985

Felt, 107 × 183
Purchased from the maker March 1986
P5363

SALMON Janice B 1961
Hat 1986

Felt, Diameter 20
Sewn into headband: *Salmon*
Purchased from the maker March 1986
P5361

RIE Lucie 1902–1995
Bowl[24] 1957

Porcelain, with sgraffito decoration through manganese (accidental splash of white glaze on rim), Diameter 17.1
Impressed on base: 🖃
Accessioned March 1957
C554

RIE Lucie 1902–1995
Salad Bowl[27] 1957

Stoneware, with white glaze showing brown flecks and dark brown rim
Diameter 22.4
Impressed on base: 🖃
Accessioned February 1957
C561

SALMON Janice B 1961
Floor Cover 1985

Felt, 180 × 166
Purchased from the maker March 1986
P5364

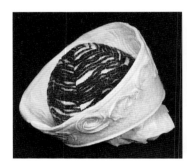

SALMON Janice B 1961
Hat 1986

Felt, Diameter 26
Sewn into headband: *Salmon*
Purchased from the maker March 1986
P5362

RIE Lucie 1902–1995
Vase[25] 1957

Porcelain, with sgraffito decoration through manganese, Height 14.2
Impressed on base: 🖃
Accessioned March 1957
C555

RIE Lucie 1902–1995 :
COPER Hans 1920–1981
Cup and Saucer

Stoneware, with white glaze and brown rim
Cup: height 6.3; Saucer: diameter 13.9
Impressed on base of cup: ⊕ and 🖃
Saucer: no markings
Accessioned March 1957
C562A (cup), C562B (saucer)

SALMON Janice B 1961
Wall Hanging with Appliqué 1986

Felt, 77 × 56.5
Purchased from the maker March 1986
P5360

SUTTIE Angus 1946–1993
Cheese Dish 1985

Stoneware, decorated with coloured glazes and lustres
Overall size: 14.4 × 33.4 × 26.8
Purchased from Anatol Orient October 1985
P5314 (detail illustrated)

Suttie Angus 1946–1993
Plate 1985

Stoneware, decorated with coloured
glazes, Diameter 31.5
Purchased from Crafts Council Shop at
the V & A November 1985

P5332

Suttie Angus 1946–1993
Vessel with Blue and White Top
1991

Stoneware, decorated with coloured
glazes, Height 58
Inscribed on base: SUTTIE
Purchased from the maker September
1991

P5968 (colour plate 66)

Taplin Guy B 1939
Merganser 1986

Painted driftwood, 8 × 27.5 × 8
Carved on underside: GUY TAPLIN 9
MERGANSER
Purchased from British Crafts Centre
April 1986

P5372

Tchalenko Janice B 1942
Jug 1981

Reduced stoneware, decorated with
coloured glazes, trailed, sponged and
painted, Height 36
Purchased from the maker February
1986

P5345

Suttie Angus 1946–1993
Mug with Ring 1985

Stoneware, decorated with coloured
glazes, Height 19
Signed on base in black marker-pen:
ANGUS 1985
Purchased from the maker December
1985

P5333

Taplin Guy B 1939
Preener 1986

Driftwood, 17 × 46 × 19
Carved on underside: 7 PREENER GUY
TAPLIN
Purchased from British Crafts Centre
April 1986

P5370

Taplin Guy B 1939
Teal 1986

Painted driftwood, 12 × 19 × 13
Carved on underside: 8 TEAL GUY
TAPLIN
Purchased from British Crafts Centre
April 1986

P5373

Tchalenko Janice B 1942
Oval Platter 1986

Reduced stoneware, decorated with
coloured glazes, trailed, sponged and
painted, Width 41.5
Purchased from the maker February
1986

P5346

Suttie Angus 1946–1993
Tall Bottle 1985

Stoneware, decorated with coloured
glazes, Height 44
Inscribed on base: ANGUS 1985
Purchased from the maker February
1986

P5344

Taplin Guy B 1939
Shorebird 1986

Painted driftwood, with metal rod and
sea-shell, Height 27 (with base)
Carved on underside of bird:
8 SHOREBIRD GUY TAPLIN
Purchased from British Crafts Centre
April 1986

P5371

Tchalenko Janice B 1942
Jug 1976

Reduced stoneware, decorated with
coloured glazes, trailed and painted
Height 36
Purchased from Collection Gallery,
Ledbury September 1985

P5306

Tchalenko Janice B 1942
Bowl 1986

Reduced stoneware, decorated with
coloured glazes, trailed, sponged and
painted, Diameter 29
Purchased from the maker February
1986

P5347

TCHALENKO Janice B 1942
Large Bowl 1986

Reduced stoneware, decorated with
coloured glazes, trailed, sponged and
painted, Diameter 41
Purchased from the maker February
1986
P5348

TUCKER Sian B 1958
Long Kimono Jacket 1985/86

Wool and silk, painted with acid dyes
Length 108
Purchased from the maker March 1986
P5355

TUCKER Sian B 1958
Wall Hanging 1985/86

Wool, painted with acid dyes, 205 × 134
Painted in fabric lower R: *Sian Tucker*
Purchased from the maker March 1986
P5358

WARDELL Sasha B 1956
Bowl 1985

Bone china, with coloured design
Diameter 18
Inscribed on base: *SKW 85*
Purchased from the maker October 1985
P5325

TCHALENKO Janice B 1942
Red Bowl 1988

Reduced stoneware, decorated with
coloured glazes, trailed, sponged and
painted, Diameter 28.6
Purchased from the maker February
1992
P6044 (colour plate 67)

TUCKER Sian B 1958
Shirt and Pants 1985/86

Wool and silk, painted with acid dyes
Shirt: length 79; Pants: length 100
Purchased from the maker March 1986
P5356

WARDELL Sasha B 1956
Tall Vase 1985

Bone china, with coloured design
Height 18
Inscribed on base: *SKW 85*
Purchased from the maker October 1985
P5323

WARDELL Sasha B 1956
Jug 1985

Bone china, with coloured design
Height 23
Inscribed on base: *SKW 85*
Purchased from the maker October 1985
P5326

TCHALENKO Janice B 1942
Red Platter 1988

Reduced stoneware, decorated with
coloured glazes, trailed, sponged and
painted, Width 48.7
Purchased from the maker February
1992
P6045 (colour plate 67)

TUCKER Sian B 1958
Scarf 1985/86

Wool, painted with acid dyes, 200 × 44
Purchased from the maker March 1986
P5357

WARDELL Sasha B 1956
Vase 1985

Bone china, with coloured design
Height 10
Inscribed on base: *SKW 85*
Purchased from the maker October 1985
P5324

WHITING Geoffrey 1919–1988
Teapot[28]

Stoneware, with brown iron glaze
Height 12.9
Impressed below spout: (AD) (C)
Accessioned December 1956
C551

WHITING Geoffrey 1919–1988
Teapot[28]

Stoneware, with red-brown iron glaze
Height 12.6
Impressed below spout: 〔Aᴿ〕 Ⓐ
Accessioned December 1956
C552

YASUDA Takeshi B 1943
Teapot 1992

Stoneware, decorated with coloured
glazes and embossing
Height 23.3
Purchased from the maker February
1993
P6140

WILLIAMS Christopher B 1949
Clown/Melon 1988

Blown glass, cut and sandblasted
35 × 20 × 14
Purchased from the maker February
1989
P5625

WOOD Ruth Mary 1899–1980
"Honour a Physician"
(Ecclesiasticus 38:1–8)[29] *c.*1945/46

Inscription on vellum, 54 × 35.5
Accessioned March 1946
C55

Notes on the Craft Collection

1. When the dates attributed to Michael Cardew's works conflict in the published sources, the dates given are those cited in the maker's autobiography.

2. C292A, C292B
Illustrated in colour, plate 8: *Michael Cardew A Portrait* by Garth Clark (Faber and Faber, 1978).
Illustrated in black and white, plate 22: *Michael Cardew, A Pioneer Potter; An Autobiography* (William Collins Sons & Co. Ltd., 1988).

3. C297
Illustrated in black and white, plate 50: *Artist-Potters in England* by Muriel Rose (Faber and Faber, 1955).
Illustrated in black and white, page 48: *Michael Cardew A Collection of Essays with an Introduction by Bernard Leach* (Crafts Advisory Committee, 1976).
Illustrated in black and white, plate 23: *Michael Cardew, A Pioneer Potter; An Autobiography* (William Collins Sons & Co. Ltd., 1988).

4. C473
Illustrated in black and white, page 47: *Michael Cardew A Collection of Essays with an Introduction by Bernard Leach* (Crafts Advisory Committee, 1976).

5. C473, C468, C469
The Berkeley Galleries, London, which held an exhibition of Cardew's stoneware pottery in November 1950, is a likely purchase source for these pieces.

6. C528
Illustrated in black and white, plate 82: *Artist-Potters in England* by Muriel Rose (Faber and Faber, 1955).

7. C549
Illustrated in black and white, page 87: *Hans Coper* by Tony Birks (Sainsbury Centre for Visual Arts, University of East Anglia, Norwich, 1983).

8. C548
Illustrated in black and white, page 94: *Hans Coper* by Tony Birks (Sainsbury Centre for Visual Arts, University of East Anglia, Norwich, 1983).

9. C47
A work of the same title is listed 73 in the catalogue of *The Arts and Crafts Exhibition Society Fiftieth Anniversary Exhibition*, held at the Royal Academy November–December 1938.

10. NZ.XIII.4, NZ.XIV.9, C90
These works carry both the maker's and the Winchcombe Pottery's seals.
The Winchcombe Pottery was set up in 1926 by Michael Cardew at Greet in the Cotswolds. He was keen to revive the country pottery tradition, aiming to produce slipware in quantities large enough to facilitate the sale of reasonably-priced items – cider jars, jugs, bowls etc. – for domestic use. In 1936 Ray Finch became Cardew's first pupil. Like Cardew, he believed in the production of good quality functional ware. In 1939 he became Manager of the Pottery, and in 1946 he purchased the Pottery from Cardew. The Winchcombe Pottery continues to produce a wide range of reduced wood fired stoneware.

11. C52
Listed 145 in the catalogue of *Exhibition 20 by The Arts and Crafts Exhibition Society*, held at the Royal Academy February–March 1946. The sales price in the catalogue accords with the Craft Collection's ledger entry for this work.

12. C53
An untitled appliqué panel by Margaret Kaye is listed 653 in the catalogue of *Exhibition 20 by The Arts and Crafts Exhibition Society*, held at the Royal Academy February–March 1946. The sales price in the catalogue accords with the Craft Collection's ledger entry for **Lion**.

13. As all Walter Keeler's work is made over a span of years, and some pieces are still in production, it is difficult to date pieces exactly.

14. C505
Listed 86 in the catalogue of *The Art of Bernard Leach, A Loan Retrospective Exhibition*, held at the Victoria and Albert Museum March–May 1977.

15. C91
Illustrated in black and white on the catalogue cover of *The Leach Pottery 1920–1946* exhibition, held at the Berkeley Galleries, London June 1946.
Illustrated in black and white, plate 17: *Artist-Potters in England* by Muriel Rose (Faber and Faber, 1955).
Listed 95 in the catalogue of *The Art of Bernard Leach, A Loan Retrospective Exhibition*, held at the Victoria and Albert Museum March–May 1977.

16. C123
Illustrated in black and white, plate 16: *Artist-Potters in England* by Muriel Rose (Faber and Faber, 1955).

17. C504
The Craft Collection ledger entry attributes this work to Bernard Leach, and the purchase price would seem to support this. It is, however, the only Bernard Leach piece in the Craft Collection which does not carry both Bernard Leach and St. Ives seals.

18. In 1920 Bernard Leach and Shoji Hamada set up the Leach Pottery at St. Ives, building the first oriental type climbing kiln in Europe. Their aim was to produce affordable pottery, maintaining high standards of form, glaze, decoration and quality. As the Pottery grew in size and reputation, it drew student apprentices from all over the world. At first, the pots produced were individual pieces, sold through one-man exhibitions to enthusiasts and collectors, but as time went on, the work became known to a wider public, and a steady demand for good, hand-made tableware developed. The Pottery is now owned by Bernard Leach's widow, Janet Leach.

19. C475
Illustrated in black and white plate 63, page 69: *Lucie Rie A Survey of Her Life and Work*, edited by John Houston with photographs by David Cripps (Crafts Council, 1981).

20. C479
Illustrated in black and white plate 66, page 69: *Lucie Rie A Survey of Her Life and Work*, edited by John Houston with photographs by David Cripps (Crafts Council, 1981).

21. C537
Illustrated in black and white plate 82, page 71: *Lucie Rie A Survey of Her Life and Work*, edited by John Houston with photographs by David Cripps (Crafts Council, 1981).

22. C545
Illustrated in black and white plate 94, page 73: *Lucie Rie A Survey of Her Life and Work*, edited by John Houston with photographs by David Cripps (Crafts Council, 1981).

23. C553
Illustrated in colour plate 8, page 38: *Lucie Rie A Survey of Her Life and Work*, edited by John Houston with photographs by David Cripps (Crafts Council, 1981).

24. C554
Illustrated in black and white plate 89, page 72: *Lucie Rie A Survey of Her Life and Work*, edited by John Houston with photographs by David Cripps (Crafts Council, 1981).

25. C555
Illustrated in black and white plate 97, page 73: *Lucie Rie A Survey of Her Life and Work*, edited by John Houston with photographs by David Cripps (Crafts Council, 1981).

26. C556
Illustrated in black and white plate 90, page 72: *Lucie Rie A Survey of Her Life and Work*, edited by John Houston with photographs by David Cripps (Crafts Council, 1981).

27. C561
Illustrated in black and white plate 231, page 91: *Lucie Rie A Survey of Her Life and Work*, edited by John Houston with photographs by David Cripps (Crafts Council, 1981).

28. C551, C552
A possible purchase source is the Design Centre, where an exhibition of Whiting's teapots was held in 1956.

29. C55
A work of the same title is listed 221 in the catalogue of *Exhibition 20 by The Arts and Crafts Exhibition Society*, held at the Royal Academy February–March 1946. The sales price in the catalogue accords with the Craft Collection's ledger entry for **'Honour a Physician'**.

† Included in the British Council's *Exhibition of Modern British Crafts* which opened 20 May 1942 at the Metropolitan Museum of Art, New York, and subsequently toured to nine cities in the USA, and five in Canada. Muriel Rose's report of 15 November 1945 to the Fine Arts (General) Committee emphasises the universal appeal of the exhibition: "I feel that the outstanding value of this show from the point of view of the British Council has been its appeal to a much wider cross-section of the public than those reached by exhibitions of paintings. An exhibit showing domestic objects, pottery and glass, chairs and tables, books and textiles, particularly when grouped in arrangements suggesting rooms, does not present the barrier of strangeness many feel in regard to modern painting, and a collection of this kind is at once closely related to the daily life of visitors of every sort."

In addition to the general public, visitors included practising artists, university students, teachers of art, handiwork and home economics, buyers and assistants from the furnishing departments of the big city stores, and teachers and nurses from hospital departments of occupational therapy, with their patients. Many museums had purchased works for their collections, and there was much praise for "the fine quality both of raw material and workmanship in the exhibits . . . the fact that the furniture was as well finished at the back or inside the drawers as in front, the attention given to making the reverse of the quilting and needlework almost indistinguishable from the front . . ."

The summary of press comments appended to the report includes the following extract from *Retailing* 15 June 1942 – a viewpoint which illustrates the general response to the exhibition: "There is a feeling of hope in the exhibition of British Crafts now being shown at the Metropolitan Museum of Art. Whilst most of it is familiar . . . there is a good bit in the craft tradition suggesting the work of our own New England and Southern Mountain pioneers . . . it spells the hope that people, despite war, despite terrific upheavals, will go down making useful and worthwhile things".

‡ Included in the British Council's *Exhibition of Rural Handicrafts from Great Britain* which toured New Zealand 1946–48, and was subsequently shown in venues throughout Australia.

CLIFF Clarice 1899–1972
Odilon shape Teapot 1932

From **Bizarre** range, designed by
Clarice Cliff; manufactured by Newport
Pottery Co. Ltd.[1]
Earthenware, with hand painted
Nasturtium pattern, Height 12
Purchased from Alfies Antique Market,
London January 1993
P6133

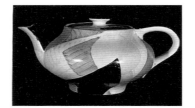

COOPER Susie 1902–1995
'Art Deco' style Teapot c.1928

Designed by Susie Cooper;
manufactured by Johnson Bros.
(Hanley) Ltd[4]
Earthenware, with hand painted pattern
of geometric circles, squares and
triangles in yellow, orange, grey and
black, Height 10
Purchased from Alfies Antique Market,
London January 1993
P6135

EMPIRE PORCELAIN CO.[5]
Teapot c.1953

Earthenware, with dove-grey glaze
Height 13
Purchased from The Ginnel Gallery,
Manchester May 1993
P6187

GRAY'S POTTERY (A E GRAY &
CO. LTD.)
Jug[7] 1947

Earthenware, hand painted splashed
purple lustre, with a print of **New
Steam Coach** (from an engraved
copper plate) over glaze, Height 10
Accessioned August 1947
C110

CLIFF Clarice 1899–1972
Bon Jour shape Teapot 1933

Designed by Clarice Cliff;
manufactured by A J Wilkinson Ltd.[2]
Cream earthenware, with hand painted
decoration in beige, brown and green
Height 14
Purchased from Alfies Antique Market,
London January 1993
P6134

COOPER Susie 1902–1995
Kestrel shape Teapot 1932/33

Designed by Susie Cooper;
manufactured by The Susie Cooper
Pottery Ltd.
Earthenware, with **Grey Leaf** pattern
Height 14
Purchased from Alfies Antique Market,
London January 1993
P6137

GRAY'S POTTERY (A E GRAY &
CO. LTD.)[6]
Plate with Scalloped Edges[7] 1947

Earthenware, splashed purple lustre,
with a print of a ship (from an engraved
copper plate) over glaze, Diameter 26.7
Accessioned August 1947
C108

GRAY'S POTTERY (A E GRAY &
CO. LTD.)
Bowl[7] 1947

Earthenware, hand painted splashed
purple lustre, with a print of **The
Shipwright's Arms** (from an engraved
copper plate) over glaze, Diameter 27.2
Accessioned August 1947
C112 (colour plate 59)

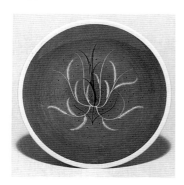

COOPER Susie 1902–1995
Large Round Plate[†]

Designed by Susie Cooper;
manufactured by The Susie Cooper
Pottery Ltd.[3]
Earthenware, with olive-green glaze and
under glaze centre decoration
Diameter 38
Accessioned August 1947
C107

COOPER Susie 1902–1995
Rex shape Teapot 1936

Designed by Susie Cooper;
manufactured by The Susie Cooper
Pottery Ltd.
Earthenware, aerographed in green
with **Crescents** pattern, Height 14
Purchased from Alfies Antique Market,
London January 1993
P6136

GRAY'S POTTERY (A E GRAY &
CO. LTD.)
Jug[7] 1947

Earthenware, hand painted splashed
purple lustre, with a print of a ship
(from an engraved copper plate) over
glaze, Height 12.7
Accessioned August 1947
C109

HOGAN James 1883–1948
Sherry Glass c.1942

From a specimen set of table glasses[8]
with knob stem in design number 9245
Designed by James Hogan;
manufactured by James Powell & Sons
Ltd.,[9] Height 11.5
Accessioned December 1945
C77D

HOGAN James 1883–1948

Liqueur Glass[1] *c.*1942

From a specimen set of table glasses[8] with knob stem in design number 9245

Designed by James Hogan; manufactured by James Powell & Sons Ltd., Height 8.3

Accessioned December 1945

C77E

MURRAY Keith 1892–1981

Vase *c.*1948

Designed by Keith Murray; manufactured by Josiah Wedgwood & Sons Ltd. [13]

Cream earthenware, covered with a layer of slip, stained green; incised decoration, Height 20.3

Accessioned December 1948

C197

POWELL Harry J 1853–1922

Port Glass

From a specimen set of table glasses in design number 8317

Designed by Harry J Powell; manufactured by James Powell & Sons Ltd., Height 12.9

Accessioned December 1945

C78D

RAVILIOUS Eric 1903–1942

Coronation Mug[1] 1936[14]

Designed by Eric Ravilious; manufactured by Josiah Wedgwood & Sons Ltd.

Cream earthenware, printed sepia, with green band and pale red decoration Height 10.2

Accessioned December 1948

C188

J & G MEAKIN LTD.[10]

Studio Ware Teapot 1955

Earthenware, with maroon glaze Height 14

Purchased from The Ginnel Gallery, Manchester May 1993

P6183

MURRAY Keith 1892–1981

Bowl *c.*1948

Designed by Keith Murray; manufactured by Josiah Wedgwood & Sons Ltd.

Cream earthenware, covered with a layer of slip, stained green; fluted shape Diameter 16.8

Accessioned December 1948

C199

POWELL Harry J 1853–1922

Liqueur Glass

From a specimen set of table glasses in design number 8317

Designed by Harry J Powell; manufactured by James Powell & Sons Ltd., Height 10.2

Accessioned December 1945

C78F

RAVILIOUS Eric 1903–1942

Alphabet Mug[1] 1937

Designed by Eric Ravilious; manufactured by Josiah Wedgwood & Sons Ltd.

Earthenware, printed black, banded blue, Height 8.3

Accessioned December 1948

C193

MURRAY Keith 1892–1981

Tumbler Vase

Designed by Keith Murray; manufactured by Stevens & Williams[11]

Engraved glass, with lines and dots decoration, Height 20.3

Purchased from Dunbar Hay Ltd., London October 1948[12]

C271

POWELL Harry J 1853–1922

Claret Glass

From a specimen set of table glasses in design number 8317

Designed by Harry J Powell; manufactured by James Powell & Sons Ltd., Height 13.5

Accessioned December 1945

C78C

JAMES POWELL & SONS LTD.

Bowl

Glass, with optic ribbing and white threaded decoration, Diameter 12.7

Purchased from Dunbar Hay Ltd., London October 1948

C267

RAVILIOUS Eric 1903–1942

Boat Race Day Bowl[1] 1938

Designed by Eric Ravilious; manufactured by Josiah Wedgwood & Sons Ltd.

Earthenware, printed sepia, royal blue, blue, golden orange and pink decoration, Diameter 30.5

Accessioned December 1948

C191

RAVILIOUS Eric 1903–1942
Dessert Plate in Garden Design
1938

Designed by Eric Ravilious;
manufactured by Josiah Wedgwood &
Sons Ltd.

Earthenware, printed sepia centre and
border, enamelled blue, Diameter 23
Purchased from Britannia, Grays
Antique Market, London March 1992
P6049 & P6050 [2 plates]

RAVILIOUS Eric 1903–1942
Coronation Mug introduced 1952[14]

From a revised Eric Ravilious design;
manufactured by Josiah Wedgwood &
Sons Ltd.

Earthenware, printed sepia, pink lustre
band and lemon yellow decoration
Height 10.2
Accessioned March 1953
AN543

TAIT Jessie B 1928
Fashion shape Teapot 1954

Zambesi pattern designed by Jessie Tait;
manufactured by W R Midwinter Ltd.
Earthenware, with hand painted
decoration; black under glaze, red
over glaze, Height 12
Purchased from The Ginnel Gallery,
Manchester May 1993
P6185

WEBB CORBETT LTD.
Champagne Saucer

Cut and engraved glass, with polished
and matt decoration in pattern number
12662, Height 14.2
Accessioned August 1947
C117

RAVILIOUS Eric 1903–1942
Vegetable Dish in Garden Design
1938

Designed by Eric Ravilious;
manufactured by Josiah Wedgwood &
Sons Ltd.

Earthenware, printed sepia centre and
border, enamelled blue, Diameter 25.2
Purchased from Britannia, Grays
Antique Market, London March 1992
P6051

SEENEY Enid B 1932
Metro shape Teapot 1957

Homemaker pattern[15] designed by Enid
Seeney; manufactured by Ridgway
Potteries Ltd.[16]
Earthenware, with decoration printed
under glaze, Height 13
Purchased from Alfies Antique Market,
London March 1993
P6182

TAIT Jessie B 1928
Fashion shape Teapot 1954

Cherokee pattern designed by Jessie
Tait; manufactured by W R Midwinter
Ltd.
Earthenware, with hand painted
decoration under glaze, Height 17
Purchased from The Ginnel Gallery,
Manchester May 1993
P6186

WEBB CORBETT LTD.
Goblet

Cut and engraved glass, with polished
and matt decoration in pattern number
12384, Height 20
Accessioned August 1947
C118

RAVILIOUS Eric 1903–1942
Garden Implements Jug[†] 1939

Designed by Eric Ravilious;
manufactured by Josiah Wedgwood &
Sons Ltd.

Earthenware, printed sepia, painted
purple and pink lustre and lined black
Height 19.6
Accessioned December 1948
C189

TAIT Jessie B 1928
Stylecraft shape Teapot 1953

Red Domino pattern designed by Jessie
Tait; manufactured by W R Midwinter
Ltd.[17]
Earthenware, with hand painted
decoration over glaze, Height 11
Purchased from The Ginnel Gallery,
Manchester May 1993
P6184

WEBB CORBETT LTD.[18]
Goblet

Cut and engraved glass, with polished
and matt decoration in pattern number
12662, Height 25
Accessioned August 1947
C116

JOSIAH WEDGWOOD & SONS
LTD.
Leaf Dish

Cream earthenware, Length 14
Purchased from Dunbar Hay Ltd.,
London September 1948
C150A & C150B [2 dishes]

JOSIAH WEDGWOOD & SONS LTD.
Leaf Dish
Cream earthenware, Length 21
Purchased from Dunbar Hay Ltd.,
London September 1948
C151A

JOSIAH WEDGWOOD & SONS LTD.
Leaf Dish
Cream earthenware, Diameter 22
Purchased from Dunbar Hay Ltd.,
London September 1948
C151B

JOSIAH WEDGWOOD & SONS LTD.
Leaf Dish
Cream earthenware, Diameter 19.6
Purchased from Dunbar Hay Ltd.,
London September 1948
C152A & C152B [2 dishes]

JOSIAH WEDGWOOD & SONS LTD.
Cruet
Containing mustard pot, salt cellar and
pepper pot
Cream earthenware, boat shaped, with
ram's head at prow and serpent's head
at stern, Width 26.7
Mustard pot: height 8.3
Salt cellar: height 3.2
Pepper pot: height 8.3
Purchased from Dunbar Hay Ltd.,
London September 1948
C153A−E

JOSIAH WEDGWOOD & SONS LTD.
Coffee Can and Saucer
Cream earthenware, decorated with an
embossed design, Can: height 5.8
Saucer: diameter 12.9
Purchased from Dunbar Hay Ltd.,
London September 1948
C154A (can), C154B (saucer)
& C155A (can), C155B (saucer)
[2 coffee cans and saucers]

JOSIAH WEDGWOOD & SONS LTD.
Coffee Can and Saucer
Cream earthenware, with a ridged
design, Can: height 5.8
Saucer: diameter 12.9
Purchased from Dunbar Hay Ltd.,
London September 1948
C156A (can), C156B (saucer)

JOSIAH WEDGWOOD & SONS LTD.
Custard Pot and Lid
Cream earthenware
Height 12.7
Purchased from Dunbar Hay Ltd.,
London September 1948
C158A (pot), C158B (lid)
& C159A (pot), C159B (lid)
[2 custard pots and lids]

JOSIAH WEDGWOOD & SONS LTD.
Covered Bowl on Foot with Lid
Cream earthenware
Height 18.4
Purchased from Dunbar Hay Ltd.,
London September 1948
C161A (bowl), C161B (lid)

JOSIAH WEDGWOOD & SONS LTD.
Plate[19]
Earthenware, silver lustre, with etched
and painted design, Diameter 23.5
Purchased from Dunbar Hay Ltd.,
London September 1948
C167A & C167B [2 plates]

JOSIAH WEDGWOOD & SONS LTD.
Bowl
Black jasper, with white bas relief
decoration of **Acanthus and Bell** motif
Diameter 17.8
Purchased from Dunbar Hay Ltd.,
London September 1948
C175

JOSIAH WEDGWOOD & SONS LTD.
Bowl
Black basalt, with ribbed decoration
Diameter 18.8
Purchased from Dunbar Hay Ltd.,
London September 1948
C176

JOSIAH WEDGWOOD & SONS LTD.
Bowl
Black basalt, with ribbed decoration
Diameter 13.5
Purchased from Dunbar Hay Ltd.
London September 1948
C177

JOSIAH WEDGWOOD & SONS
LTD.
Set of Carpet Bowls [20] *c.*1938
(manufactured for Dunbar Hay Ltd.,
London)

Eight bowls in three different patterns,
plus a jack in a separate pattern, with
presentation box
Bowls: diameter 8; Jack: diameter 6
Accessioned October 1949

C395 A–I

WILLIAMS-THOMAS, Joseph S
1848–1932
Covered Vase[†]

Designed by Joseph S Williams-
Thomas; manufactured by Stevens &
Williams
Glass on square foot, with cut festoon
pattern, Height 30.5
Accessioned December 1945

C87

Notes on the Production Ware in the Craft Collection

1. Newport Pottery Company Ltd., Burslem 1920–1964; taken over 1964 by W R Midwinter Ltd.

2. A J Wilkinson Ltd., Burslem 1885–1964; taken over 1964 by W R Midwinter Ltd.

3. The Susie Cooper Pottery Ltd., Burslem and Tunstall 1929–1980; Susie Cooper's companies became part of the Wedgwood Group in 1966.

4. Johnson Brothers (Hanley) Ltd., 1883–1968; taken over 1968 by the Wedgwood Group.

5. Empire Porcelain Co., Stoke-on-Trent 1896–1987; 'Ltd.' added circa 1963; part of Qualcast Group 1958–1967.

6. A E Gray & Co. Ltd., Hanley 1907–1961; now part of The Portmeirion Potteries Ltd.

7. The Gray's Pottery pieces are not thought to be part of sets. It is likely that when they were made in 1947, they were destined for immediate export, since the Utility regulations were then still in force in Britain. Only plain white or ivory ware was allowed on the Home Market from 1942–1952. The splashed lustre ware sold in large quantities in North America – the ship on **The Shipwright's Arms** is flying a US flag.

8. Designed for use in British embassies.

9. James Powell & Sons 1835–1980, Whitefriars Glass Works, Wealdstone, Middlesex; became James Powell (Whitefriars) Ltd., 1919–1962, and Whitefriars Glass Ltd. 1962–1980.

10. J & G Meakin Ltd., Hanley 1851–1968; merged 1968 with W R Midwinter Ltd.

11. Stevens & Williams; founded as Silvers, Mills and Stevens; became Stevens & Williams in 1847, moved to the present site, Brierley Hill Glass Works, Staffordshire in 1870; became Royal Brierley Crystal Ltd. in 1985.

12. Dunbar Hay Ltd., London was established in 1936 by Cecilia Dunbar Kilburn (later Lady Sempill) in partnership with Athole Hay. Their policy was to promote the very best of British decorative art and design, and the venture flourished until the war. The shop closed in 1940; it was bombed in 1942 and the business was never revived. Thus it is rather puzzling to see the British Council's records of purchases made from Dunbar Hay Ltd. as late as 1948/49. A possible explanation may lie in Lady Sempill's established links with the British Council; she had contributed an essay to the catalogue of the inaugural craft exhibition in 1942, and was subsequently one of the appointed expert advisers on purchases of craft for the Collection. It is perhaps reasonable, therefore, to assume that the British Council may have been given access to the remaining stock of Dunbar Hay Ltd.

13. Josiah Wedgwood & Sons Ltd., established 1759 in Burslem; a vase works was opened in Etruria, where all production was centralised in the early 1770s. The Etruria factory was demolished around 1963. Wedgwood became Waterford Wedgwood in 1986; now Waterford Wedgwood Group.

14. Designed and produced in 1936, the mug was withdrawn on the King's abdication. It was revised in 1937 for the Coronation of George VI and Queen Elizabeth, and again in 1952 for the Coronation of Queen Elizabeth II.

15. The **Homemaker** range was sold only through Woolworths until 1967/8.

16. Ridgway Company, Stoke-on-Trent, founded 1792; renamed Ridgway Potteries Ltd. in 1955; and incorporated into Allied English Potteries 1964; merged with Doulton and Company Ltd. 1971; now Royal Doulton Ltd.

17. W R Midwinter Ltd., Burslem 1910–1987; taken over (with subsidiaries A J Wilkinson Ltd., Newport Pottery Company Ltd., and J & G Meakin Ltd.) by the Wedgwood Group 1970.

18. Webb Corbett Ltd., Coalbournhill Glass Works, Amblecote, Stourbridge, founded 1897; taken over 1969 by Royal Doulton Crystal.

19. Both pieces bear the characteristics of the School of Freehand Painting, established around 1906 at Josiah Wedgwood & Sons Ltd., Etruria, by Alfred and Louise Powell.

20. This set of bowls is first mentioned in the Wedgwood Factory records (earthenware books) in October 1938.

† Included in the British Council's *Exhibition of Modern British Crafts* which opened 20 May 1942 at the Metropolitan Museum of Art, New York and subsequently toured the USA and Canada.

ABBOTT Mike B 1963
Estate Agent and Cityscape Brooch

Brass and enamel paint, Length 13.5
Purchased from the maker February 1991
P5872

ABBOTT Mike B 1963
Sun Mask Brooch

Brass and enamel paint, Length 9
Purchased from the maker February 1991
P5875

ADAM Jane B 1954
Black Necklace

Thirteen black Kelim beads, Length 47
Purchased from the maker January 1991
P5843

ARKELL Julie B 1955
Spoon Brooch

Card, Polyfilla, china and paste stone
Length 23
Purchased from the maker April 1991
P5921

ABBOTT Mike B 1963
Heli-beetle Brooch (articulated)

Brass and enamel paint, Length 7
Purchased from the maker February 1991
P5873

ADAM Jane B 1954
Large Twisted Brooch

Anodised aluminium and ink, Width 12
Purchased from the maker January 1991
P5841

ADAM Jane B 1954
Blue Paisley Brooch

Anodised aluminium, ink and applied gold leaf, Width 9.5
Purchased from the maker January 1991
P5844

ARKELL Julie B 1955
Fork Brooch

Card, Polyfilla, china and paste stone
Length 21
Purchased from the maker April 1991
P5922

ABBOTT Mike B 1963
Aeroplane Brooch

Brass and enamel paint, Width 10.5
Purchased from the maker February 1991
P5874

ADAM Jane B 1954
Earrings

Anodised aluminium and ink, Length 7
Purchased from the maker January 1991
P5842

ARKELL Julie B 1955
Chandelier Earrings

Painted card and beads, Drop 12.5
Purchased from the maker April 1991
P5920

ARKELL Julie B 1955
Dog Brooch

Card, Polyfilla and china, Width 13
Purchased from the maker April 1991
P5923

ARKELL Julie B 1955
Tiara

Card, Polyfilla and paste stones
Width 18
Purchased from the maker April 1991
P5924

CHATWIN, Peter B 1945 :
MARTIN, Pamela B 1949
Long Brooch

Hand-dyed sycamore, with gold leaf
Length 11.5
Purchased from the makers March 1991
P5901

COUSENS Cynthia B 1956
Brooch

Silver, Length 14.5
Purchased from the maker February
1991
P5878

ELLWOOD Kim B 1956
Spiky Fossil Brooch

Steel and enamel, Length 10
Purchased from the maker February
1991
P5868

CHATWIN, Peter B 1945 :
MARTIN, Pamela B 1949
Pendant

Hand-dyed sycamore, with silk cord
Length 37.5; diameter 7
Purchased from the makers March 1991
P5899

CHATWIN, Peter B 1945 :
MARTIN, Pamela B 1949
Stud Earrings

Hand-dyed sycamore, with gold leaf
Length 6
Purchased from the makers March 1991
P5902

COUSENS Cynthia B 1956
Earrings

Silver, Length 4.5
Purchased from the maker February
1991
P5879

ELLWOOD Kim B 1956
Red Aeroplane Brooch

Steel and enamel, Width 7.5
Purchased from the maker February
1991
P5869

CHATWIN, Peter B 1945 :
MARTIN, Pamela B 1949
Bangle

Hand-dyed sycamore, with gold leaf
Diameter 13.5
Purchased from the makers March 1991
P5900

COUSENS Cynthia B 1956
Pendant Earrings

Silver, Drop 5
Purchased from the maker February
1991
P5877

COUSENS Cynthia B 1956
Earrings

Silver, Length 3
Purchased from the maker February
1991
P5880

ELLWOOD Kim B 1956
Long-legged Man Brooch

Steel, with gold leaf, Length 15
Purchased from the maker February
1991
P5870

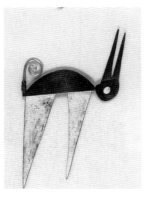

ELLWOOD Kim B 1956
Creature Brooch

Steel, with gold leaf, Length 6
Purchased from the maker
February 1991
P5871

FINLAY Anne B 1953
Bangle

PVC, Diameter 13
Purchased from the maker March 1991
P5910

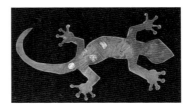

HESLOP Maura B 1963
Lizard Brooch

Steel and silver, Width 9
Purchased from the maker March 1991
P5888

HESLOP Maura B 1963
Creature Brooch

Steel and polyester resin, Width 8
Purchased from the maker March 1991
P5891

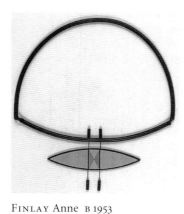

FINLAY Anne B 1953
Neckpiece

PVC, rubber and steel, Diameter 21.5
Purchased from the maker March 1991
P5908

FINLAY Anne B 1953
Brooch

Acrylic and PVC, Length 7
Purchased from the maker March 1991
P5911

HESLOP Maura B 1963
Fishes Brooch

Steel and polyester resin, Length 5
Purchased from the maker March 1991
P5889

HESLOP Maura B 1963
Dragon Brooch

Steel and polyester resin, Length 13
Purchased from the maker March 1991
P5892

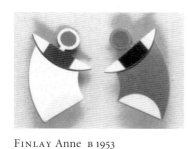

FINLAY Anne B 1953
Earrings

Stainless steel, laminate and PVC
Length 3.6
Purchased from the maker March 1991
P5909

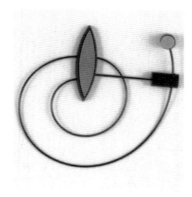

FINLAY Anne B 1953
Brooch

PVC, nylon, steel and rubber, Length 6
Purchased from the maker March 1991
P5912

HESLOP Maura B 1963
Animal Brooch

Steel and silver, Width 8.5
Purchased from the maker March 1991
P5890

HINKS Leah B 1964
Necklace with bronze lustre

Glazed and lustred porcelain, Length 72
Purchased from the maker April 1991
P5913

HINKS Leah B 1964
Blue-green and Mother of Pearl Necklace

Glazed and lustred porcelain, Length 62
Purchased from the maker April 1991
P5914

HINKS Leah B 1964
Pink Whirly Hairpin

Glazed and lustred porcelain, Length 19
Purchased from the maker April 1991
P5917

KRINOS Daphne B 1955
Leaf Earrings with Perspex Circles

Perspex, silver and gold, Drop 8
Purchased from the maker February 1991
P5863

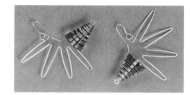

McKIBBIN Marlene B 1953
Tapered Earrings with Turned Discs

Acrylic and silver, Drop 7
Purchased from the maker February 1991
P5881

HINKS Leah B 1964
Aquamarine and Mother of Pearl Earrings

Glazed and lustred porcelain, Drop 7
Purchased from the maker April 1991
P5915

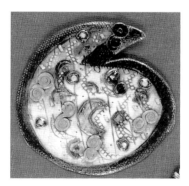

HINKS Leah B 1964
Moon Brooch

Glazed and lustred porcelain
Diameter 10.5
Purchased from the maker April 1991
P5918

KRINOS Daphne B 1955
Brooch

Oxidised silver, with gold leaf, Length 11
Purchased from the maker February 1991
P5864

McKIBBIN Marlene B 1953
Long Necklace

Dyed and patterned acrylic and silver
Length 54
Purchased from the maker February 1991
P5882

HINKS Leah B 1964
Green and Pink Hairpin

Glazed and lustred porcelain, Length 18
Purchased from the maker April 1991
P5916

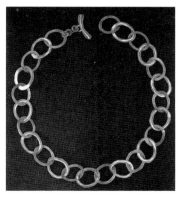

KRINOS Daphne B 1955
Neck Chain

Oxidised silver and fine gold, Length 49
Purchased from the maker February 1991
P5862

KRINOS Daphne B 1955
Ring

Silver, gold and garnet, Diameter 2.5
Purchased from the maker February 1991
P5865

McKIBBIN Marlene B 1953
Leopard Bangle

Dyed and patterned acrylic
Diameter 10
Purchased from the maker February 1991
P5883

MᴄKɪʙʙɪɴ Marlene B 1953
Ear Studs

Clear acrylic and silver, Diameter 1.5
Purchased from the maker February
1991
P5884

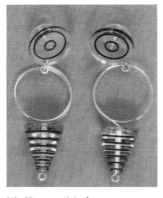

MᴄKɪʙʙɪɴ Marlene B 1953
Tapered Earrings

Acrylic and silver, Length 7.5
Purchased from the maker February
1991
P5887

Mᴀᴛʜᴇʀ Carol B 1965
Grasshopper Brooch

Brass and enamel paint, Width 8
Purchased from the maker March 1991
P5896

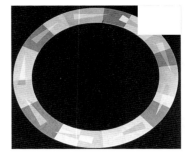

Nɪᴄᴢᴇᴡsᴋɪ Peter B 1948
Neckpiece

Dyed veneers, Diameter 27
Purchased from the maker April 1986
P5375

MᴄKɪʙʙɪɴ Marlene B 1953
Bangle

Clear acrylic and silver, Diameter 10
Purchased from the maker February
1991
P5885

Mᴀᴛʜᴇʀ Carol B 1965
Fish Earrings

Brass and enamel paint, Width 5
Purchased from the maker March 1991
P5894

Mᴀᴛʜᴇʀ Carol B 1965
Stag Beetle Brooch (articulated)

Brass and enamel paint, Length 11
Purchased from the maker March 1991
P5897

Nɪᴄᴢᴇᴡsᴋɪ Peter B 1948
Brooch

Dyed veneers, Length 4.5
Purchased from the maker April 1986
P5376

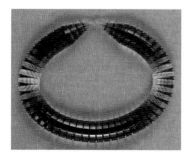

MᴄKɪʙʙɪɴ Marlene B 1953
Bangle with Tapers

Acrylic, Diameter 10.5
Purchased from the maker February
1991
P5886

Mᴀᴛʜᴇʀ Carol B 1965
Vole Brooch (articulated)

Brass and enamel paint, Length 8.5
Purchased from the maker March 1991
P5895

Mᴀᴛʜᴇʀ Carol B 1965
**Mermaid with Seahorse and Fish
Brooches** (articulated)

A set in three pieces
Brass and enamel paint
Height of Mermaid: 11
Purchased from the maker March 1991
P5898

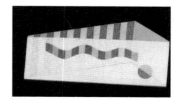

Nɪᴄᴢᴇᴡsᴋɪ Peter B 1948
Brooch

Dyed veneers, Width 6
Purchased from the maker April 1986
P5377

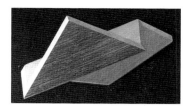

NICZEWSKI Peter B 1948
Brooch

Dyed veneers, Width 9.5
Purchased from the maker April 1986
P5378

ROBERTS Geoff B 1953
Fish with Shell Corsage

Acrylic and coloured foil, Length 15.5
Purchased from the maker May 1991
P5938

ROBERTS Geoff B 1953
Set of Three Fish Brooches

Acrylic and coloured foil
Length: Fish A: 27.5; Fish B: 22; Fish C:
18
Purchased from the maker May 1991
P5941A–C

SHERBURNE Annie B 1957
Water Halo

Wood, enamel paint and sequins
Diameter 30
Purchased from the maker February
1991
P5904

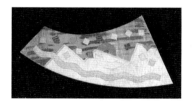

NICZEWSKI Peter B 1948
Brooch

Dyed veneers, Width 8.5
Purchased from the maker April 1986
P5379

ROBERTS Geoff B 1953
Bangle

Acrylic and coloured foil, Diameter 12.5
Purchased from the maker May 1991
P5939

ROBERTS Geoff B 1953
Fish Earrings

Acrylic and coloured foil, Curved Fish:
length 9; Straight Fish: length 12.5
Purchased from the maker May 1991
P5942

SHERBURNE Annie B 1957
Fantasia Earrings

Wood, enamel paint, beads and coins
Length 6
Purchased from the maker February
1991
P5905

ROBERTS Geoff B 1953
Quiver of Fish Neckpiece

Acrylic and coloured foil, Diameter 38.5
Purchased from the maker May 1991
P5937

ROBERTS Geoff B 1953
Anklet

Acrylic and coloured foil, Diameter 13.5
Purchased from the maker May 1991
P5940

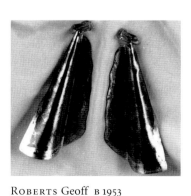

ROBERTS Geoff B 1953
Shell Earrings

Acrylic and coloured foil, Length 10.5
Purchased from the maker May 1991
P5943

SHERBURNE Annie B 1957
Brooch

Wood, enamel paint and sequins
Width 9.5
Purchased from the maker February
1991
P5906

SHERBURNE Annie B 1957
Brooch

Wood, enamel paint and sequins
Width 12
Purchased from the maker February
1991
P5907

SHILLITO Ann Marie B 1947
Slotted Brooch

Titanium and steel, Width 12
Purchased from the maker June 1991
P5957

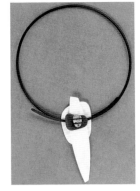

SLATER Louise B 1956
Black Neckpiece

Acrylic, pebbles and nylon wire
Diameter 18
Purchased from the maker June 1991
P5944

SLATER Louise B 1956
Shield Brooch

Acrylic, pebbles and nylon wire
Width 16.5
Purchased from the maker June 1991
P5947

SHILLITO Ann Marie B 1947
Dragon Necklace

Titanium and steel, with bead and silk
Length 43
Purchased from the maker June 1991
P5955

SHILLITO Ann Marie B 1947
Brooch

Aluminium, Width 12.5
Purchased from the maker June 1991
P5958

SLATER Louise B 1956
Black Earrings

Acrylic, pebbles and nylon wire
Length 9
Purchased from the maker June 1991
P5945

STEWART Gordon B 1963
'Of Last Iron' Brooch

Photo-etched aluminium, Height 11
Purchased from the maker July 1991
P5951

SHILLITO Ann Marie B 1947
Dragon Earrings

Titanium and steel, with silk, Drop 10
Purchased from the maker June 1991
P5956

SHILLITO Ann Marie B 1947
Feather Brooch

Titanium, Length 9
Purchased from the maker June 1991
P5959

SLATER Louise B 1956
Round Brooch

Acrylic, pebbles and nylon wire
Diameter 7
Purchased from the maker June 1991
P5946

STEWART Gordon B 1963
'Evelyn' Brooch

Photo-etched aluminium, Height 10.5
Purchased from the maker July 1991
P5952

STEWART Gordon B 1963
'Bob' Brooch

Photo-etched aluminium, Height 15.5
Purchased from the maker July 1991
P5953

THOMPSON Karina B 1965
Peacock Brooch

Feathers, fabric and metal, Length 26.5
Purchased from the maker October 1991
P5973

VICHI Clara B 1962
Cuff-links

Oxidised silver and brass, Depth 1.8
Purchased from the maker January 1991
P5836

VICHI Clara B 1962
Ring

Oxidised silver, Diameter 2.3
Purchased from the maker January 1991
P5839

STEWART Gordon B 1963
'John and Murray' Brooch

Photo-etched aluminium, Height 9
Purchased from the maker July 1991
P5954

THOMPSON Karina B 1965
Red Sword Brooch

Feathers, fabric and metal, Length 23.5
Purchased from the maker October 1991
P5974

VICHI Clara B 1962
Brooch

Painted wood, with silver, Length 8
Purchased from the maker January 1991
P5837

VICHI Clara B 1962
Brooch

Silver and brass, Width 5.5
Purchased from the maker January 1991
P5840

THOMPSON Karina B 1965
Cockerel Brooch

Feathers, fabric and metal, Length 24
Purchased from the maker October 1991
P5972

THOMPSON Karina B 1965
Rosette Brooch

Fabric and metal, Width 15.5
Purchased from the maker October 1991
P5975

VICHI Clara B 1962
Drop Earrings

Oxidised silver, Drop 4.5
Purchased from the maker January 1991
P5838

Note

With the exception of Peter Niczewski's work which was purchased for inclusion in the circulating exhibition *Cloth Clay Wood* (1987–1993), the jewellery in the Craft Collection was acquired in 1991 to form the circulating exhibition *All that glisters . . . New Jewellery in Britain* (mounted 1992, still on tour at the time of writing).

56 EDWARD BAWDEN
Wallpaper 'Tree and Cow' 1927
P6218 & P6219

57 MICHAEL CARDEW
Bowl *c.*1949/50
C469

58 HANS COPER
left: **Pot** *c.*1955
C548
right: **Waisted Pot** *c.*1954
C549

59 GRAY'S POTTERY
(A E GRAY & CO. LTD.)
Bowl 1947
C112

60 BERNARD LEACH
Large Jar with Handle 1945
C91

61 BERNARD LEACH
Large Jar *c.*1948–52
C501

62 CAROL McNICOLL
Coffee Set 1991
P6033

63 KATE MALONE
**Starfish in the Belly of
a Sea Urchin** 1989
P5801

64 LUCIE RIE
Bowl 1957
C553

65 LUCIE RIE
Bowl 1957
C556

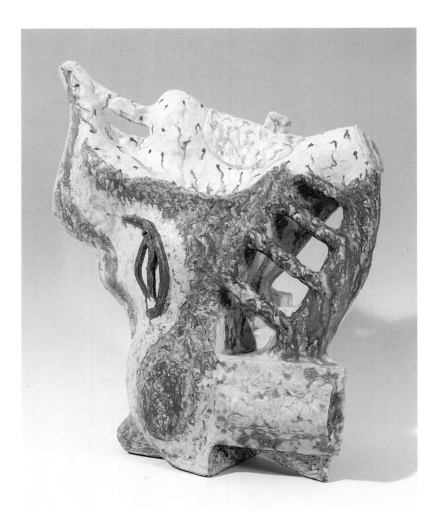

66 ANGUS SUTTIE
**Vessel with Blue and
White Top** 1991
P5968

67 JANICE TCHALENKO
left: **Red Platter** 1988
P6045
right: **Red Bowl** 1988
P6044

PART VI : Circulating Exhibitions on Tour 1984–94

Visual Arts Department's activities include a programme of circulating exhibitions drawn primarily from work in the British Council Collection. Such exhibitions are designed for long-term touring, and are shown in countries which have little direct access to original works of British art. Most are accompanied by an illustrated catalogue, leaflet or poster.

The following circulating exhibitions have been assembled from works in the British Council Collection.

The Rake's Progress

William Hogarth (1697–1764)
David Hockney (B 1937)

Two versions of The Rake's Progress: 16 etchings and aquatints by David Hockney; eight prints by William Hogarth.

Leaflet, with a black and white cover illustration, containing one black and white illustration, a catalogue essay by Edward Lucie-Smith, and brief biographical notes.
(No ISBN)

Originated 1966; disbanded 1993
Belgium, Bulgaria, Colombia, Egypt, Hungary, Malta, Netherlands, Oman, Poland, Portugal, Spain.

Bill Brandt Photographs

60 photographs, ranging from the artist's documentary works of the 1930s to his portraits of the 1970s.

Catalogue, with a black and white illustration on the back cover, containing 12 black and white plates, and an introduction by Aaron Scharf.
(No ISBN)

Originated 1973; disbanded 1994
Argentina, Chile, Colombia, Cuba, Cyprus, former Czechoslovakia, Denmark, Ecuador, Egypt, Ireland, Mexico, Norway, Peru, Poland, Spain, Sweden, Turkey.

Figuration and Fantasy Contemporary British Prints

50 prints by Ivor Abrahams, Peter Blake, Boyd & Evans, Richard Hamilton, David Hockney, R B Kitaj, Tom Phillips and William Tillyer.

Catalogue (French text only), with a black and white cover illustration, containing eight black and white plates, an introduction by M. Sandiford, and brief biographical notes.
(No ISBN)

Originated 1974; disbanded 1987
Israel, Philippines, Senegal, former Yugoslavia, Zimbabwe.

Contemporary British Drawings

Selected by Norbert Lynton: 90 drawings by Clive Barker, Peter Blake, Bernard Cohen, Michael Craig-Martin, Rita Donagh, Barry Flanagan, David Hockney, John Hoyland, Paul Huxley, Bill Jacklin, Peter Joseph, Jeremy Moon, Martin Naylor, Tom Phillips, Carl Plackman, Bridget Riley, Michael Sandle, Colin Self, Richard Smith, Ian Stephenson, William Tucker and John Walker. (This exhibition formed the British Section of the 1975 São Paulo Bienal).

Catalogue, containing 18 black and white plates, four colour plates, an introduction by Norbert Lynton, and brief biographical notes.
(No ISBN)

Originated 1975; disbanded 1990
Australia, Canada, Hong Kong, Iraq, Malaysia, New Zealand, Philippines, Singapore, Thailand.

British Artists' Prints 1972–77

Selected by Pat Gilmour: 56 prints by Norman Ackroyd, Richard Allen, Anthony Benjamin, Victor Burgin, Patrick Caulfield, Bernard Cohen, Alan Cox, Robyn Denny, Phillippa Ecobichon, Hamish Fulton, Roy Grayson, Alan Green, Anthony Gross, Richard Hamilton, Tim Head, Patrick Hughes, Ben Johnson, Allen Jones, Kim Lim, Eduardo Paolozzi, Victor Pasmore, Tom Phillips, Bridget Riley, Michael Rothenstein, Norman Stevens, William Tillyer, Joe Tilson, Ian Tyson, Shelagh Wakely and John Walker.

Catalogue, containing four black and white illustrations, ten black and white plates, and an introduction by Pat Gilmour.
(No ISBN)

Originated 1977; disbanded 1989
Bahrain, Canada, Egypt, Iraq, Jordan, Morocco, Qatar, Spain, United Arab Emirates.

Colour in British Painting

Selected by Alan Bowness: 34 small paintings by Frank Auerbach, Stephen Buckley, Bernard Cohen, Alan Davie, Terry Frost, John Golding, Patrick Heron, Ivon Hitchens, John Hoyland, John Hubbard, Allen Jones, Leon Kossoff, Tom Phillips, William Scott, Jack Smith, Richard Smith, Ian Stephenson and William Turnbull.

Catalogue (dual text: Portuguese and Spanish), containing one colour plate, 11 black and white full plates, six black and white half-plates, an introduction by Alan Bowness and brief biographical notes.
(No ISBN)

Originated 1977; disbanded 1985
Hungary, former Yugoslavia.

Tom Phillips Graphics

37 prints from the early 1960s to the late 1970s.

Catalogue (French text only), with a cover illustration in colour, containing 12 black and white plates, six black and white illustrations, essays by David Bindman and Jean-Yves Bosseur, commentaries by the artist, and biographical and bibliographical details.
(No ISBN)

Originated 1979; disbanded 1990
Chile, Colombia, Cyprus, Ecuador, Greece, Iraq, Jamaica, Peru, Spain.

Photography as Medium

Selected by Teresa Gleadowe: 36 photographs by Keith Arnatt, Marc Chaimowicz, Hamish Fulton, Fay Godwin, Brian Griffin, Tim Head, Paul Hill, John Hilliard, Sharon Kivland, Simon Read, Al Vandenberg and Boyd Webb.

Catalogue, with a black and white cover illustration, containing 12 black and white plates, one black and white illustration, an introduction and entries by Teresa Gleadowe, and a selected bibliography.
(No ISBN)

Originated 1980; disbanded 1986
Denmark, Spain.

David Hockney The Blue Guitar

20 etchings and aquatints by David Hockney illustrating the poem by Wallace Stevens, *The Man with the Blue Guitar*.

Poster only.

Originated 1982; disbanded 1993
Belgium, Brazil, Canada, Chile, Colombia, Ecuador, Federal Republic of Germany, Greece, Hungary, Jordan, Luxembourg, Mexico, New Zealand, Turkey, Venezuela, former Yugoslavia.

Forty Years of British Sculpture

Selected by Muriel Wilson: 17 small sculptures and 33 works on paper by Robert Adams, Kenneth Armitage, Anthony Caro, Lynn Chadwick, Hubert Dalwood, Barbara Hepworth, Bernard Meadows, Denis Mitchell, Henry Moore, Gavin Scobie and William Turnbull.

Catalogue, containing 13 black and white plates, an introduction by Muriel Wilson, and biographical notes. (No ISBN)

Originated 1982; extended 1994 to form *A Changing World Fifty Years of Sculpture from the British Council Collection*, still on tour (see separate entry under this title).
Canada, Cyprus, Egypt, Estonia, Greece, India, Latvia, Lithuania, New Zealand, Philippines, Russia, South Africa, Turkey, Ukraine, former Yugoslavia.

Fay Godwin Landscape Photographs

Selected by the artist and Brett Rogers: 44 photographs 1972–1982.

Catalogue, with a black and white cover illustration, containing 14 black and white plates, an introduction by Brett Rogers, an essay by Ian Jeffrey and biographical and bibliographical notes.
ISBN 0 86355 006 1

Originated 1983; disbanded 1994
Bangladesh, Belgium, Brazil, Brunei, Chile, China, Colombia, Denmark, Ecuador, Finland, France, Federal Republic of Germany, Hong Kong, Hungary, India, Indonesia, Italy, Luxembourg, Malaysia, Peru, Singapore, Sweden, Thailand.

New Works on Paper

Selected by Mary Rose Beaumont: 59 works on paper by Roger Ackling, Frank Auerbach, Sandra Blow, Derek Boshier, John Carter, David Connearn, Eileen Cooper, Ken Dingwall, Edwin Easydorchik, John Edwards, Stephen Farthing, Noel Forster, Alan Green, Maggi Hambling, Richard Hamilton, Ron Haselden, Paul Hempton, Gerard Hemsworth, Carole Hodgson, David Inshaw, Albert Irvin, Andrzej Jackowski, Richard Kidd, Ken Kiff, Peter Kinley, Ian McKeever, Robert Mason, George Meyrick, Michael Murfin, Victor Newsome, Ken Oliver, Liz Pannett, Deanna Petherbridge, Michael Porter, Paula Rego, Bruce Russell, Michael Sandle, Kevin Sinnott, Richard Smith, Euan Uglow, Michael Upton, Stephen Willats, Victor Willing and Laetitia Yhap.

Catalogue, with a black and white cover illustration, containing nine black and white plates, and an introduction by Mary Rose Beaumont.
ISBN 0 901618 97 7

Originated 1983; disbanded 1992
Australia, Belgium, Bulgaria, Cyprus, German Democratic Republic, Luxembourg, New Zealand, Poland, Romania, former Soviet Union, Turkey.

Urban Images

Selected by Muriel Wilson: 54 prints by Norman Ackroyd, Adrian Bartlett, Paul Bristow, Chloë Cheese, Frank Connelly, Christopher Corr, Michael Fell, David Freed, P R Garriock, Phil Griffin, Glynn Boyd Harte, David Hepher, Ben Johnson, John Mackechnie, Tim Mara, Bill Meyer, Jack Miller, Terence Millington, Derek Mynott, Brendan Neiland, Chris Orr, Chris Plowman, Margaret Priest, Pat Schavarien, Alyson Stoneman, Richard Walker, Derek Wilkinson and Albany Wiseman.

Leaflet, with a black and white cover illustration, and an essay by Judith Collins.
ISBN 0 901618 98 5

Originated 1983; disbanded 1989
China, Ghana, Malawi, Nigeria, Pakistan, Turkey, Zimbabwe.

David Hockney Grimm's Fairytales

39 etchings by David Hockney, illustrating the fairytales of the Brothers Grimm.

Leaflet, with a black and white cover illustration, containing the artist's comments taken from an interview reproduced in the Victoria and Albert Museum's 1972 exhibition catalogue of the same title.
(No ISBN)

Originated 1984, still on tour
Belarus, Belgium, Bulgaria, Canada, Cyprus, Egypt, Federal Republic of Germany, German Democratic Republic, Hong Kong, India, Iraq, Israel, Jordan, Luxembourg, Malaysia, Oman, Philippines, Qatar, Russia, Singapore, Sweden, Thailand, Turkey, Ukraine.

Sculptors' Drawings

18 drawings by Tony Cragg, John Davies, Barry Flanagan, Nigel Hall, Michael Kenny, John Maine, David Nash, Carl Plackman, Michael Sandle, William Tucker and Shelagh Wakely.

Catalogue, with a black and white cover illustration, containing 11 black and white plates, an introduction by John McEwen, and biographies.
ISBN 0 86355 010 X

Originated 1984; disbanded 1987
Japan, Spain.

Cloth Clay Wood

Selected by Muriel Wilson: 60 works – textile pieces by Janet Bolton, Susie Freeman, Geraldine St. Aubyn Hubbard, Janice Salmon, Sian Tucker; ceramics by Walter Keeler, Sara Radstone, Angus Suttie, Janice Tchalenko, Sasha Wardell; works in wood by Ray Key, Peter Niczewski, Jim Partridge, Howard Raybould and Guy Taplin.

Catalogue, with colour illustrated covers, containing four colour plates, an introduction by Martina Margetts, and entries by Muriel Wilson.
Spanish and English editions
(No ISBN)

Originated 1987; disbanded 1993
Belgium, Brunei, Chile, Colombia, Ecuador, Korea, Malaysia, Oman, Peru, Singapore, Thailand, Turkey, Venezuela.

Inscriptions and Inventions British Photography in the 1980s

Selected by Ian Jeffrey and Brett Rogers: 47 photographs by Keith Arnatt, Laurence Cutting, Peter Fraser, Paul Graham, Ron O'Donnell, Martin Parr, Jem Southam, Boyd Webb, Richard Wentworth and Verdi Yahooda.

Catalogue, with a cover illustration in colour, containing 11 colour plates, one black and white plate, an introductory essay by Ian Jeffrey, entries by Brett Rogers, black and white photographs of the artists, and biographies.
ISBN 0 86355 050 9

Originated 1987; disbanded 1992
Belgium, former Czechoslovakia, Denmark, German Democratic Republic, Italy, Luxembourg, Norway, Poland, former Soviet Union, Sweden, former Yugoslavia.

Cries & Whispers New Works for the British Council Collection

Selected by Lewis Biggs: 20 paintings and large works on paper by Terry Atkinson, Tony Bevan, Vivien Blackett, Steven Campbell, Eileen Cooper, Graham Crowley, Ken Currie, Micky Donnelly, Graham Durward, Stephen Farthing, Andrzej Jackowski, Ansel Krut, Christopher Le Brun, Jock McFadyen, Lisa Milroy, Paula Rego, Andrew Stahl, Mark Wallinger and Adrian Wiszniewski.

Catalogue, with a cover illustration in colour, containing 19 colour plates, an introduction and entries by Lewis Biggs, and full biographical and bibliographical details.
ISBN 0 86355 063 0

Originated 1988; still on tour
Argentina, Australia, Brazil, Chile, Ecuador, Hong Kong, Korea, Malaysia, New Zealand, Philippines, Singapore, Spain, Turkey.

Henry Moore Etchings and Lithographs 1949–1984

Selected by Ann Elliott and David Mitchinson: 80 prints by Henry Moore, drawn from works presented to the British Council by the artist in 1984.

Catalogue, with colour illustrated covers, containing nine colour plates, 15 black and white plates, 79 black and white illustrations, essays on Moore's life and graphic work by David Mitchinson, and a listing of 100 selected monographs.
ISBN 0 86355 066 5

Originated 1988; disbanded 1992
Belarus, Bulgaria, former Czechoslovakia, Estonia, Latvia, Lithuania, Malaysia, Philippines, Russia, Singapore, Thailand, Ukraine, Zimbabwe.

Henry Moore Portfolio Prints 1950–1981

Selected by Ann Elliott and David Mitchinson: 60 prints from 13 individual portfolios from the Henry Moore Gift to the British Council in 1984.

Leaflet/poster, with one large colour poster image, 19 black and white illustrations, an essay by David Mitchinson divided between portfolio sections, a bibliographical note, and a black and white photograph of the artist.
(No ISBN)

Originated 1987; disbanded 1993
Australia, Brazil, Canada, Chile, Colombia, Peru, Venezuela.

Artists' Choice

A portfolio of 48 prints by 48 artists, published by the Royal College of Art Printmaking Course to mark the College's 150th anniversary.

Poster only, each print reproduced in colour.

Originated 1989; still on tour
The Bahamas, Barbados, Bolivia, Brazil, Chile, Colombia, Ecuador, Jamaica, Mexico, Peru, Venezuela.

For a Wider World: Sixty Works in the British Council Collection

Selected by Andrea Rose: works by Kenneth Armitage, Frank Auerbach, Edward Burra, Jeffery Camp, Anthony Caro, Patrick Caulfield, Helen Chadwick, Tony Cragg, Richard Deacon, Barry Flanagan, Lucian Freud, Gilbert and George, Harold Gilman, Spencer Gore, Roger Hilton, David Hockney, Howard Hodgkin, Gwen John, David Jones, Anish Kapoor, Phillip King, R B Kitaj, Leon Kossoff, Peter Lanyon, Richard Long, Henry Moore, Paul Nash, Ben Nicholson, Eduardo Paolozzi, Eric Ravilious, Bridget Riley, William Roberts, Sean

Scully, Walter Richard Sickert, Matthew Smith, Richard Smith, Stanley Spencer, Graham Sutherland, John Tunnard, Edward Wadsworth, Boyd Webb and Bill Woodrow.

Catalogue, with a cover illustration in colour, containing 60 colour plates, an introduction and entries by Andrea Rose, and biographical and bibliographical notes compiled by James Bustard and Emily Feaver.
ISBN 0 86355 102 5

Originated 1990; disbanded 1992
Argentina, Bulgaria, Luxembourg, Ukraine.

Henry Moore Mother and Child Etchings and Small Sculpture

The artist's final portfolio of 30 etchings and aquatints, accompanied by five maquettes.

Catalogue/leaflet, with colour illustrated covers, containing 11 black and white illustrations, an essay by Julian Stallabrass, a biographical note, and a black and white photograph of the artist.
(No ISBN)

Originated 1990; disbanded 1993
Bahrain, Cyprus, Egypt, Greece, Israel, Italy, Malta, Morocco, Oman, Turkey, United Arab Emirates.

Scottish Artists' Prints

Selected by Margaret Mackay: 47 prints by John Bellany, Steven Campbell, Ken Currie, Gwen Hardie, Peter Howson, Bruce McLean, Kate Whiteford and Adrian Wiszniewski.

Leaflet, containing five colour illustrations, five black and white illustrations, and an introduction and entries by Margaret Mackay.
(No ISBN)

Originated 1990; still on tour
Belgium, Bulgaria, Canada, Croatia, Poland, Romania, Scotland, Slovenia, Turkey.

De-Composition Constructed Photography in Britain

Selected by Andrea Rose and Brett Rogers: 29 large scale photographic works by Lea Andrews, Keith Arnatt, Helen Chadwick, Hannah Collins, Calum Colvin, Tim Head, Ron O'Donnell, Mari Mahr, Helen Sear and Boyd Webb.

Card folder, with colour illustrated covers, containing ten colour A5 cards, and an introduction by Andrea Rose.
ISBN 0 86355 117 3

Originated 1991; still on tour
Argentina, Brazil, Chile, Colombia, Ecuador, Peru, United States of America, Venezuela, Wales.

Paula Rego Nursery Rhymes

25 etchings and aquatints from the portfolio Nursery Rhymes published 1989, and six additional Nursery Rhyme etchings of the same year.

Poster only.

Originated 1991; still on tour
Brazil, Canada, Chile, Colombia, Mexico, Peru, Portugal, Spain.

All that glisters ... New Jewellery in Britain

Selected by Muriel Wilson: 90 pieces by Mike Abbott, Jane Adam, Julie Arkell, Peter Chatwin and Pamela Martin, Cynthia Cousens, Kim Ellwood, Anne Finlay, Maura Heslop, Leah Hinks, Daphne Krinos, Marlene McKibbin, Carol Mather, Geoff Roberts, Annie Sherburne, Ann Marie Shillito, Louise Slater, Gordon Stewart, Karina Thompson and Clara Vichi.

Catalogue, with colour illustrated covers, containing 12 colour plates, 22 black and white illustrations, and an introduction and entries by Muriel Wilson.
ISBN 0 86355 141 6

Originated 1992; still on tour
Bahrain, India, Indonesia, Malaysia, Philippines, Saudi Arabia, Singapore, Sri Lanka, Thailand.

Out of the Wood British Woodcuts & Wood Engravings 1890–1945

Selected by Simon Brett: 61 woodcuts and wood engravings by John Buckland Wright, Edward Gordon Craig, Eric Daglish, John Farleigh, Robert Gibbings, Eric Gill, Barbara Greg, Joan Hassall, Gertrude Hermes, Blair Hughes-Stanton, Norman Janes, David Jones, Sydney Lee, Clare Leighton, Iain Macnab, Guy Malet, Henry Moore, Thomas Sturge Moore, John Nash, Paul Nash, Agnes Miller Parker, Claughton Pellew, John Platt, Gwen Raverat, Bernard Rice, Charles Ricketts, Charles Shannon, George Soper, Charles Tunnicliffe, Leon Underwood and Clifford Webb.

Catalogue, with black and white illustrated covers, containing 50 black and white illustrations, an essay, entries and a glossary of technical terms by Simon Brett.
ISBN 0 86355 118 1

Originated 1992; still on tour
Australia, India, Kenya, Sri Lanka, Zambia, Zimbabwe.

Peter Blake Alphabet

A series of 26 screenprints, one for each letter of the alphabet.

Poster only, each print reproduced in colour.

Originated 1992; still on tour
Bulgaria, Czech Republic, Egypt, Hong Kong, Malaysia, Morocco, Philippines, Singapore, Slovakia.

A Changing World Fifty Years of Sculpture from the British Council Collection

Works selected by Diana Eccles and Joanna Gutteridge were added to Forty Years of British Sculpture to form this exhibition: 37 sculptures by Robert Adams, Kenneth Armitage, Reg Butler, Anthony Caro, Lynn Chadwick, Tony Cragg, Michael Craig-Martin, Hubert Dalwood, Richard Deacon, Barry Flanagan, Tim Head, Barbara Hepworth, Shirazeh Houshiary, Anish Kapoor, Richard Long, David Mach, Bernard Meadows, Denis Mitchell, Henry Moore, David Nash, Eduardo Paolozzi, Tim Scott, William Turnbull, Boyd Webb, Alison Wilding and Bill Woodrow.

Catalogue, with a cover illustration in colour, containing 37 colour plates, eight black and white illustrations, an introduction by Norbert Lynton, and biographical notes.
English and Russian editions
ISBN 0 86355 256 0 (English)
ISBN 0 86355 257 9 (Russian)

Originated 1994; still on tour
Russia.

Out of Print British Printmaking 1946–1976

Selected by Richard Riley: 75 prints by Peter Blake, Derek Boshier, Patrick Caulfield, Geoffrey Clarke, Henry Cliffe, Prunella Clough, Robert Colquhoun, Merlyn Evans, Terry Frost, William Gear, Alan Green, Richard Hamilton, S W Hayter, Patrick Heron, David Hockney, Howard Hodgkin, Allen Jones, R B Kitaj, Peter Lanyon, Robert MacBryde, John Minton, Henry Moore, Ben Nicholson, Eduardo Paolozzi, Victor Pasmore, Peter Phillips, Ceri Richards, Michael Rothenstein, William Scott, Colin Self, Richard Smith, Joe Tilson, William Turnbull and Bryan Wynter.

Catalogue, with a cover illustration in colour, containing 16 colour plates, 76 black and white illustrations, an introduction by Bryan Robertson, entries and a glossary of technical terms by Richard Riley, and a bibliography.
ISBN 0 86355 233 1

Originated 1994; still on tour
Belgium, France.

The following circulating exhibitions were assembled from works on loan to the British Council, supplemented by works from the British Council Collection.

Patrick Caulfield Prints 1964–1983

68 prints on loan from Waddington Graphics; updated and extended to 77 prints, including five from the British Council Collection, and subsequently re-titled Patrick Caulfield Prints 1964-1987.

Leaflet/poster (Portuguese text only), with one large colour poster image, an exhibition list, an essay by Bryan Robertson (reprinted from the catalogue Patrick Caulfield Prints 1964-81, published 1981 by Waddington Graphics), and a biographical note.
(No ISBN)

Originated 1985; disbanded 1990
Brazil, Chile, Portugal, Uruguay.

Howard Hodgkin Prints 1977–1983

Based on the 1985 exhibition of the same title, selected by Elizabeth Knowles for the Tate Gallery: 30 prints – 20 on loan from the artist, Bernard Jacobson, and Petersburg Press, six from the British Council Collection; updated and extended by four prints on loan from Waddington Graphics, and subseqently re-titled Howard Hodgkin Prints 1977-1988.

Catalogue (Italian text only), published 1986 by Mazzotta in collaboration with the British Council, Italy, with colour illustrated covers, containing 12 colour plates, 18 black and white plates, a preface by the British Council, an introduction by Enrico Crispolti, and biographical details.
ISBN 88 202 0638 2

Leaflet/poster with one large colour poster image, an exhibition list, a brief preface, an introduction by Teresa Gleadowe, a brief biographical note, and a black and white photograph of the artist.
Dual text edition: Portuguese and English; French and Spanish editions
(No ISBN)

Originated 1985; disbanded 1990
Brazil, Chile, Denmark, Finland, Greece, Italy, Morocco, Norway, Poland, Spain, Sweden, Uruguay.

49 Prints by Raymond Moore

Selected by the artist and Lewis Biggs: 49 photographs – 39 on loan from the artist and the Arts Council of Great Britain, ten from the British Council Collection.

Catalogue, containing seven black and white plates, a statement by the artist, a biography and a selected bibliography.
ISBN 0 86355 027 4

Originated 1986; disbanded 1990
Canada, Denmark, France, Netherlands, Spain, United States of America.

Constructed Narratives Photographs by Calum Colvin and Ron O'Donnell

Organised by The Photographers' Gallery, and toured overseas by the British Council: 20 photographs, including seven from the British Council Collection.

The catalogue *Constructed Narratives*, published 1986 by The Photographers' Gallery, in conjunction with the Stills Gallery, Edinburgh, served as the catalogue for the overseas tour; no separate British Council catalogue was produced.
ISBN 0 907879 08 X

Originated 1987; disbanded 1991
Cyprus, Federal Republic of Germany, Greece, Israel, Jordan, Portugal, Spain, Sweden.

Chris Killip In Flagrante

Based on the exhibition held at the Victoria and Albert Museum in 1988, and the publication of the same title: 50 photographs – 38 on loan from the artist, 12 from the British Council Collection. The publication *In Flagrante Chris Killip*, published 1988 by Martin Secker & Warburg Ltd., served as the main catalogue for the overseas tour.
ISBN 0 436 23356 8

Originated 1988; disbanded 1991
Belgium, Denmark, France, Federal Republic of Germany, Netherlands, Spain.

Alan Davie Works on Paper

Organised jointly by the British Council and Talbot Rice Gallery, University of Edinburgh: the exhibition was launched at Talbot Rice Gallery, comprising 40 gouaches, seven oils on paper, and 11 oils on canvas. These works were on loan from the artist, Gimpel Fils, and private collections, together with one work, **The Blond goes Gay** 1961, from the British Council Collection. The exhibition which subsequently toured the UK comprised works on paper only. The overseas tour commenced with a special showing of 31 selected works, including two from the British Council Collection, in Brussels, sponsored by BP Europe. The exhibition touring South America at the time of writing comprises 45 works on paper.

Catalogue (UK version), published jointly by the British Council and Talbot Rice Gallery, with a specially commissioned book jacket by the artist, containing 16 colour plates, four black and white illustrations, an essay by Duncan Macmillan, and an interview with the artist by Andrew Patrizio and Bill Hare.
ISBN 1 873108 05 2

Tri-lingual catalogue (French, Flemish and English) published for the Brussels showing by BP Europe, with a cover illustration in colour, containing 17 colour plates, a foreword by Andrea Rose, and a biographical summary.
No ISBN

Catalogue (Spanish edition) with the specially commissioned book jacket by the artist, 16 colour plates, four black and white illustrations, a foreword by Andrea Rose, an interview with the artist by Andrew Patrizio and Bill Hare, and a biographical summary.
ISBN 0 86355 202 1

Originated 1992; still on tour
Edinburgh, UK tour (organised by Talbot Rice Gallery) to Artspace, Aberdeen, Oriel Mostyn, Llandudno, and Ikon Gallery, Birmingham. Brussels, Argentina, Brazil, Chile, Colombia, Peru, Venezuela.

New Voices New Works for the British Council Collection

Selected by Gill Hedley and Andrea Rose: 27 works by David Austen, Keith Coventry, Ian Davenport, Jeffrey Dennis, Peter Doig, Gary Hume, Callum Innes, Elizabeth Magill, Antoni Malinowski, Julian Opie, Fiona Rae, Michael Stubbs, Suzanne Treister, Alison Turnbull, Rachel Whiteread – ten on loan from the artists, galleries and private collections, 17 from the British Council Collection.

This exhibition was first mounted in Belgium in 1992 to mark the British Presidency of the European Council of Ministers. For this showing, five sculptures from the British Council Collection by Tony Cragg, Richard Deacon, Anish Kapoor and Bill Woodrow were added. Rachel Whiteread's sculpture was shown in Belgium and Luxembourg only.

Catalogue, with colour illustrated covers, containing 20 colour plates, an introduction and entries by Gill Hedley, and comprehensive biographical and bibliographical information.
ISBN 0 86355 142 4

Originated 1992; still on tour
Belgium, Luxembourg, Turkey, Spain.

The Photographs of John Blakemore

Selected by the artist and Brett Rogers: 50 photographs – 30 on loan from the artist and Zelda Cheatle Gallery, 20 from the British Council Collection.

Catalogue, with black and white illustrated covers, containing 12 black and white plates, a preface by Brett Rogers, an essay by Val Williams (reprinted from *Inscape | John Blakemore*, published 1991 by Zelda Cheatle Press Ltd.), a biographical note, and a black and white photograph of the artist.

Portuguese and Spanish editions
(No ISBN)

Originated 1993; still on tour
Argentina, Brazil, Chile.

Anthony Caro The Cascades Sculptures

Seven sculptures from **The Cascades** series of 1989–90: six on loan from the artist, one from the British Council Collection (**Summer Table** 1990, presented by the artist in September 1994).

Catalogue, with black and white illustrated covers, containing eight black and white plates, two black and white illustrations, an essay by Tim Marlow, biographical details, and a black and white photograph of the artist.
ISBN 0 86355 221 8

Originated 1993; still on tour
Cyprus, Greece, Hungary, Romania, Turkey.

Note

These tour lists relate to the period 1984–94 and in many cases therefore do not comprise comprehensive exhibition itineraries.

Curators of the British Council Collection 1984–1994

Muriel Wilson   1979–1984

Ian Barker   1984–1985

Teresa Gleadowe   1985–1989

Andrea Rose   1989–1993

Diana Eccles was appointed Collections Manager in 1993